Dr. SPOCK
Talks with Mothers

Other books by Dr. Benjamin Spock

THE COMMON SENSE BOOK OF
BABY AND CHILD CARE
(Also published as THE POCKET BOOK OF
BABY AND CHILD CARE)

A BABY'S FIRST YEAR
(with Dr. John Reinhart)

FEEDING YOUR BABY AND CHILD
(with Dr. Miriam E. Lowenberg)

Dr. SPOCK
Talks with Mothers

Growth and Guidance

BY BENJAMIN SPOCK, M.D.

HOUGHTON MIFFLIN COMPANY BOSTON
THE RIVERSIDE PRESS CAMBRIDGE
1961

LIBRARY OF CONGRESS CATALOG CARD NUMBER: 61–13338

FIRST PRINTING
The Riverside Press
CAMBRIDGE · MASSACHUSETTS

PRINTED IN THE U.S.A.

To Mike and John

WHAT THE TALKS
ARE ABOUT

There are certain important topics in child rearing that need some explaining if parents are to understand the deeper meaning of their children's behavior and misbehavior.

Adolescence, for instance. This is a stage of development that presents lots of bewildering problems. But it's not possible to solve them with simple suggestions. If a mother is to cope wisely with a teenager who's being difficult she really needs, I think, to have an idea about what's going on in his deeper feelings — of which even he is not aware. So I've tried hard to clarify these complex matters, and I've illustrated with examples ranging from the commonplace to the morbid.

Likewise, in the 3-to-6-year-old period there are a number of topics — nightmares, phobias, sleep problems, sex play, questions about the facts of life — all of which have something to do with the strivings and anxieties in the young child's unconscious mind — and I've discussed these frankly.

Discipline — including the father's part in it — is always a highly controversial subject and no one person can really tell another how to carry it out. I've done my best to analyze some of the vital factors in it, so that parents will be in a better position to get the results that they themselves want.

But not all the chapters in this book are about psychological matters. I've taken up such questions as "How important is fresh air?" and "Why do mothers want to give their children sweets?" I've expressed my personal opinions about these, hoping that this would help mothers to come to their own sensible conclusions.

The basic material in these chapters has been drawn from some of the articles I have written for the *Ladies' Home Journal* at various times and I am indebted to the editors for permission to re-use it. However, in preparing this book the material has been expanded, brought up to date, rearranged and rewritten, so that each major theme can be presented as a meaningful whole.

I thank Houghton Mifflin for assigning Joyce Hartman to the editing of this book. Her skillful, tactful job made my work easy. I also thank Mary Bergen and Elizabeth Daunton for their wise advice when I was writing some of the original articles, and Dr. Marvin Shapiro who collaborated in the research and writing of the pieces on a child's position in the family.

BENJAMIN SPOCK, M.D.

CONTENTS

I
YOUR CHILD'S HEALTH

II
A CHILD'S POSITION IN THE FAMILY

III
DISCIPLINE AND COMPANIONSHIP

IV

BEHAVIOR PROBLEMS IN THE YOUNG CHILD

V

ATTACHMENTS AND ANXIETIES BETWEEN THREE AND SIX

VI

TURNING TO THE OUTSIDE WORLD AFTER SIX

VII

THE STRAINS OF ADOLESCENCE

Contents ::)x i (::

I

Your Child's Health

WHEN SHOULD YOU
CALL THE DOCTOR?

*Parents aren't meant
to be diagnosticians.*

"I HOPE you will find it possible to give young women advice on when to call the doctor," a mother wrote me. "Due to the doctor shortage, an attitude has grown up that I think is penalizing the children of this country. Mothers feel guilty about calling the doctor. In spite of the fact that you and others have repeatedly warned that a sniffle and a sore throat and a slight temperature can mean almost anything from a cold to scarlet fever, too often mothers do hesitate because they are afraid of seeming foolish and overanxious. I nearly fell into the same error a few weeks ago when my seven-year-old had those same symptoms, which were accompanied by a severe headache. It was the headache that made me resolve to get the doctor, and the result was what he called 'aborted meningitis.' Thanks to quick action on my doctor's part, my youngster was not very sick."

I agree vigorously that a mother who is worried about her

child's condition should telephone the doctor and not stop to wonder whether he will think it unnecessary or whether she will feel embarrassed. But if we agree on this, it only shifts the question, for many mothers, to "When should I be worried?"

The first problem — and it bothered me all the time I was writing *Baby and Child Care* — is that no two mothers are alike, naturally, and that even if a doctor could lay down a fairly safe set of rules for one parent, they wouldn't work safely for another. To take a couple of extreme examples: if I were writing only for very worrisome, overly conscientious mothers, I'd want to keep reassuring them that a lot of symptoms that sound scary *usually* don't lead to anything serious; pain behind the ear *early* in an ear infection *usually* doesn't point to mastoid disease in the ordinary sense; pain in the abdomen only *occasionally* means appendicitis, and so on. But at the opposite extreme are the very, very casual mothers. If they read those same statements they'd understand me to say that pain behind the ears doesn't mean anything, and that children never get appendicitis so you don't need to pay attention to their abdominal pains.

As a matter of fact, most parents shift from overly worrisome with their first child to overly casual with their third or fourth, which is natural and wholesome. I can still remember a generally sensible mother who called me about her fourth child's illness, saying, "I hate to bother you, but Jenny has been pretty sick for three days now with high fever and headache. Do you suppose you need to see her?" Those two symptoms together are enough to make a doctor at least think of the possibility of meningitis. I tried not to sound as alarmed as I felt and rushed out in the middle of office hours to make the home visit. (It wasn't meningitis.)

🦋 🦋 🦋

It would be handy to be able to tell parents that low fever doesn't mean much but that high fever is always more serious.

But it isn't true. To be sure, a lot of serious diseases like pneumonia, meningitis, peritonitis, mastoiditis usually have high fever, but all of them can occur with only low-grade fever. And roseola infantum, an infection of early childhood, which isn't serious at all, has typically a steady fever of 104° for three or four days before the rash breaks out.

It's worth remembering that in the early months of infancy the body tends not to react with much fever, even in the more dangerous infections. Then, with most children, somewhere around one or two years of age, a change takes place. Now the body develops a tendency to react with high fever at the start of all kinds of illnesses, mild as well as serious. Most parents know this from their own experience. A common story is that the child seems entirely well in the morning, has lost some of his appetite and pep by lunch, and has 104° at the end of the afternoon. The doctor is called, finds little in his examination except perhaps a slightly red throat. Within a day or two the fever is gone and the child is well or has only a running nose. In other words, the mildest of colds, sore throats or grippe is likely to stir up quite a fever at this age. By five or six or seven years of age most children are getting out of this high-fever-over-nothing stage. They're now more likely to start their colds and sore throats with little fever, and when they do have fever it's more apt to mean something.

In many individual illnesses you can say that the fever in the beginning of the disease is much less important than what the fever is doing after a few days. A fever that begins to climb several days after the start of an infection often shows that the disease is getting worse or that a complication has developed, whether or not there was fever at the start. This is particularly true of colds and throat infections: the increase in fever or the return of the fever raises the question of whether the cold has spread to the ears or down into the bronchial tubes (bronchitis or pneumonia, especially if there is more cough) or into the urinary system (pyelitis) or into the sinuses or neck glands. In other words, I'd make a flat statement that any fever that went

up or came back after the second day would make it imperative
to get in touch with a doctor.

☙ ☙ ☙

But aren't there any other clues for the guidance of sensible
parents, particularly those who live many miles from a doctor
and who can't reach him by telephone? I don't think there are
any that can be relied on completely, but there are a few that
may help somewhat. I'd put first the general appearance of the
child — how "sick" he looks, how prostrated, how different in
appearance and behavior from his usual healthy state. If a child
looks and acts sick, I'd try much harder to get a doctor to see
him or to bring him to the doctor than if he is eating and playing
as usual — no matter what his fever.

Next I'd like to list several particular symptoms that occur
during colds that *always* call for prompt medical attention. Perhaps the commonest is earache. Not because ear infection is
always serious — in most cases the child recovers without serious
trouble. But untreated ear infection sometimes drags on and,
when prolonged, it may leave a degree of permanent deafness.
Yet when treated promptly with one of the modern drugs, ear
infection can usually be stopped in its tracks. There is no excuse
for neglecting it.

Another symptom calling always for quick attention is hoarseness of voice or tightness of breathing. To be sure, hoarseness is
most often a sign of only a mild laryngitis that comes to nothing,
and tightness of breathing is most often due only to a mild
temporary "croup." But hoarseness and tightness, especially if
accompanied by fever, may be signs of a more dangerous laryngitis and bronchitis that call for vigorous treatment.

So far I have been discussing colds and throat infections and
their complications. These together cause probably nine tenths
of children's illnesses. Another group are the stomach and
intestinal infections which show themselves in diarrhea and

vomiting. A baby is more susceptible to them in the first two years of life and they should be treated with particular care at this age period. I think the doctor should be consulted whenever a baby's movements become definitely loose. The urgency becomes greater if the movements are watery or bloody, or if there is also vomiting, fever, or prostration. After the second birthday a mild diarrhea for a day seldom becomes more serious, but if pain or any of the other symptoms listed above should occur, the doctor should be called.

There are, of course, dozens of other diseases that affect various parts of the body, which are too complicated to discuss and most of which are too rare to be remembered. The mother who wrote the letter had the bad luck to run into meningitis, which is very infrequent. She sensed, if she did not think it out, that headache, especially severe headache, is uncommon in the early years of childhood and should always be looked into promptly. Her child probably looked sicker, too, than with most infections. It's the unusual appearance that should alert the parent — and it usually does.

Abdominal pain is complained of at the beginning of many infections, and in the young child probably means nausea in many of these cases. Stomach-ache is also common in children with feeding problems and with other worries. Appendicitis is certainly rare compared with these other causes. But it's potentially serious enough so that abdominal pain should be looked into, especially if it's an unusual complaint for this particular child and if it continues for an hour or more. (A pain that lasts a few minutes and then goes away for good is not appendicitis.)

At this point you probably feel like saying, "It all sounds too complicated and yet too incomplete to be helpful; and I doubt if I will remember it the next time my child is ill." I think that is the normal reaction. Parents aren't meant to be diagnosticians. Doctors in training don't just learn a list of diseases and their symptoms and then expect to make diagnoses. They spend four years in medical school and perhaps several more in residencies, studying the body, the bacteria that invade it, the actual organs that have been invaded, the laboratory tests for the disease, the textbook descriptions of the variations in symptoms that different cases show, and then they examine and treat dozens of cases in the hospital. By the time they enter practice they should be thoroughly familiar with pneumonia or ear infections or appendicitis, in all their usual forms, from a dozen different angles. And even so, doctors usually feel that their judgment would be so poor trying to diagnose and treat a member of their own family that practically all of them turn to other doctors for such help.

Then how can a parent with no training be expected to go very far in deciding what's serious and what isn't?

With sprains which cause swelling or continued pain or awkward use I'd call a doctor because it takes skill and sometimes an X ray to rule out a fracture. And the doctor should also be consulted about head injuries if there is even brief unconsciousness, sleepiness, vomiting, headache or continued pallor.

When a small child has swallowed or been suspected of swallowing a substance which might possibly be poisonous — and there are dozens of such in every home today — it's much safer (after briefly and energetically attempting to cause vomiting by stirring your finger around in the back of his throat) to call your doctor. If he can't be reached immediately, there are several alternatives. Many large cities now have a poison information center where you can get advice. Look up the telephone number now and write it in a handy place. If you live near a hospital, hustle over there. If you live far from a hospital, ask your doctor's secretary or the telephone operator to find another doctor for you quickly; or call the hospital yourself.

Most injuries in children are minor bruises and scratches, and parents feel unworried about these, from their own experience. When the skin is scraped or slightly cut, soap and water is the handiest first aid. But if there is a real cut that opens up, especially on the face where it may leave a scar, or a puncture wound, then the doctor should decide about the desirability of stitching or of a tetanus booster shot.

☙ ☙ ☙

I know well how apologetic parents become when calling a doctor, particularly if they themselves doubt the seriousness of the illness. I think they should do their best to get over that embarrassment. Even if they feel it's probably a foolish call, they should call anyway. Otherwise I don't see any point in having a doctor. Usually the doctor doesn't mind a "foolish question" the way the parent imagines. Even if a mother is *sure* that the doctor will be grumpy about this call, she should call anyway, if she is concerned. Obviously the child's health is more important than the doctor's or the parent's feelings.

HANDLING THE
CONVALESCENT CHILD

It's possible to be sympathetic
without being anguished.

◄◊

DURING convalescence from illness, the two problems which mothers quite often face are keeping the child contented and keeping themselves from being harassed. There may be psychological as well as physical reasons for the crossness and demandingness that so often occur.

We've learned from psychiatric work with young children that they often interpret an illness or an operation as punishment for having done something bad or for having had antagonistic thoughts toward another member of the family. A child feels as guilty about a mean thought as about an act. He assumes that in a magic way his thought can do real harm. As a matter of fact, most older children and adults carry over, unconsciously, some of this belief in their own black magic and have various superstitions for warding off the effects of dangerous thoughts. The child who is guilty about hostile feelings toward his mother says, "Step on a crack, break your mother's back." A mother knocks on wood when she says her child hasn't been sick this winter. We parents frequently suggest the idea that illnesses are induced by naughtiness. We say, "If you'd worn your rubbers as I told you to, you wouldn't have caught cold"; or "Your quarreling has given mother a headache."

While a child is sick he's probably feeling at least a bit frightened by the punishment factor, by the symptoms, and by the danger of the illness itself. This last fear he may get from his mother, who shows it in her face as she reads the thermometer, in her tone when she telephones the doctor, in her solicitousness as she cares for the child. When the worst of the illness has passed, the child begins to perk up, and this is when he's apt to become difficult. One of the human reactions to a fright which has passed is to get mad at the person who caused it. This is frequently shown by the angriness of a parent toward a child who has almost fallen out a window or nearly got himself run over. Since a young child is so apt to think of disease as a punishment and since the parent is usually thought of as the punisher, it's probable that unconsciously he holds the parent partly responsible for the illness. He may also blame her for not having protected him from any painful things the doctor had to do. A normal mother often reinforces his idea that she is somehow guilty by her unaccustomed concern, her readiness to accommodate his whims, her tolerance of his disagreeableness. Of course one of the reasons she acts this way is that she may imagine that the child became sick or had an accident through some slight carelessness on her part. The doctor wouldn't usually agree with her, but that's the way a good parent is made.

If a child thinks his mother gave him the illness for punishment and if the mother thinks she gave it to him through negligence, you can see that their misconceptions reinforce each other. As soon as the child begins to recover, he feels better in his conscience. He has paid for his sins — real or imaginary — and he sees that he's still very much alive. Whatever guiltiness the mother may have had doesn't go away quite so fast. For one thing, she realizes that the illness isn't entirely over yet.

This is where a psychological imbalance may exist for a few days. To the degree that she acts guilty — in the sense of kow-towing to him or permitting him to be tyrannical — it encourages him to blame and to punish her.

Perhaps you think I'm being too morbid. I don't mean that if feelings of guilt and blame are present they are necessarily intense. Certainly there are plenty of illnesses in which the parents remain matter-of-fact and the child remains sweet-natured. I'm only suggesting the possibility of psychological factors for those parents who regularly have trouble during convalescence.

🍃 🍃 🍃

It is wise for a mother to remind herself during any illness or injury how easy it is for her to blame herself, so that she can be on guard against acting submissive. She can inquire about the child's symptoms in a matter-of-fact tone such as the doctor uses, and not ask too often. I don't mean that she should seem indifferent or hard-boiled. It's possible to be sympathetic without being anguished.

When the child begins to be a bit demanding of service, she can put him in his place with a firm reminder that she doesn't like to be spoken to in that manner and that she has lots of other work to be done. If he scorns a drink which he asked for himself a short time before, she can suggest that he make the best of it until it is time for her to prepare something else.

If he begins climbing out of bed against orders or otherwise horsing around, it's much better for the mother to get as emphatic and masterful as she would if he were well, rather than to be too patient or to warn him anxiously about the possible worsening of the disease. A threat gives a child a choice of obeying or taking the consequences, so it is always weaker than a command.

A very practical matter is how much time the mother can

spend with the invalid. Even if she is hard pressed with work, she will want to set aside at least brief periods through the day when she can sit with him. Children (like adults) when sick are not just bored if left alone. They can't help feeling more dependent than usual. I can still remember how glad I was when my mother came to the hospital, to sit in my room and give me sips of water, after a tonsillectomy when I was twenty years old.

If the child begins to demand more attention than the mother can possibly give, then it might be a good idea for her to lay out a rather arbitrary schedule of when she can visit and when she can't. More important than the number of minutes is the tone of voice — when she announces the schedule or later when the child tries to get her to come to him outside of schedule.

When a mother is pulled two ways in her feelings about a child's demand, not wanting to give in to what seems like an unreasonable and inconvenient request but still wondering guiltily whether perhaps she ought to, her indecision is apt to show up in a hesitant or petulant or angry tone as she says "No." The child instantly detects the fact that she's not sure of her ground and he sets to work to undermine her with repeated pleas, new symptoms, self-pitying descriptions of his plight, even artful tears. The mother should try to sound cheerfully, confidently definite.

☙ ☙ ☙

Now for some practical and ingenious suggestions sent to me by a mother named Helen Thomas Irwin. She starts by saying, "Just as mamma breathes a sigh of gratitude to hear that her child is going to be all right, she is faced with two statements: 'Keep him quietly in bed for a couple of days longer'; and 'What'll I do now, mamma?' The child is soon tired of TV, crayons and games. He wants you to read him stories or to tell him again all the ones about when you were a little girl. Reading a series of children's books, especially comics, has the same effect as morphine on me. I fall asleep. I have to think of other solutions.

"Change beds often. Let him stay for a while in your bed, then the couch made into a bed, then back to his own. The change of scene is restful and makes old toys seem more interesting.

"Give him a bell, This relieves his temptation to leap out of bed to find you and you can usually hear it above the sound of the vacuum or running water.

"No matter what time of year it is, give him the box of Christmas ornaments. He can admire each one separately, fill his head with happy holiday thoughts, and possibly make a few new additions to the collection.

"When we were traveling, ornaments were a particular problem because they had to be flat and unbreakable. On the cover of favorite comic books there were usually large drawings of 'friends,' such as Little Lulu, Fox and Crow, Donald Duck. I traced some of them (using a sheet of carbon paper) onto the white cardboards which came from the laundry in shirts. Then my child colored them, cut them out, attached loops of thread and carefully put them away for the Christmas tree. They have been an enormous success. For a small child, you can cut large cardboard stars, squares and circles. These, also, can look pretty on the tree and can give him the pleasure of having made them himself.

"Give the child a pile of old magazines, not just to look at, but with a definite *plan* in view. He can 'build' a house, or a hospital. For a hospital he's going to go through the magazines and cut out all pictures of nurses, doctors, babies, medicines, flowers, beds, clocks, or anything else he'd like to have in his hospital. When he has collected a pile of pictures, you can pin them to an old screen, or to a curtain near his bed. A boy can pretend he's the head doctor giving orders from his 'office' on the pillows; a girl can be the head nurse. It's the same game with building a house, except that he finds pictures of a living room, bathroom, bedroom, food, car, and so on. A boy can build a garage.

"The button box! There are many things to do with buttons, but you will have to watch out if the child is small enough to put them into his mouth. They can be sorted and put into cups according to their ability to be jewels, or according to their color or shape. They can also be stirred with a spoon and served in doll dishes. (A gravy ladle is fun to use in serving.) They can be strung into a huge necklace or they can form designs on the bed table. Have you a wide, soft piece of elastic such as might be left over from a worn-out pajama bottom? The child can sew (or pin with safety pins) buttons on this elastic to create a fabulous button belt.

"Buttons can also serve as 'money' for points in a game or, placed in a tin candy box, become a lovely rhythm instrument for shaking while playing a phonograph record.

"Have you a junk-jewelry box into which you tossed the summer jewelry you'll never wear again and the series of lone earrings after you'd despaired of ever finding mates? Or you can give him your regular box of jewelry, removing anything of real value. My child has spent hours looking over each piece, peering inside lockets, and finally becoming an emperor by wearing all the jewelry at once plus my bed jacket and an aluminum-foil crown. This idea may not sound like much, but it has given me hours of peace.

"The silverware chest. I'll never know exactly why, but taking all the silverware out of the chest and putting it back again is fun for children.

"A box of old photographs or albums or scrapbooks. The child enjoys seeing pictures of himself especially, so his own baby book provides entertainment. You must be prepared, though, to have him look at a beautiful and youthful picture of yourself and say, 'Who's that? *You?* It doesn't look like you!'

"If it is near a holiday, there are cards to be made. These can be Christmas cards, Valentines, Easter cards, Happy St. Patrick's

Day cards, or any kind of cards. We are usually near some kind of holiday. These cards can be fancy, or just a suitable picture on a large sheet of paper — for instance, a large egg for Easter. The important thing is that they are to be considered of value and actually mailed to the people on his list. An old stand-by is to 'make lace.' He takes a plain sheet of paper and folds it a few times, then cuts out slices and half circles. When he opens the sheet, it is 'lacework' which you help him paste onto colored paper.

"Taking medicine has become unpleasant by now. He's well enough to resist, to threaten to vomit. He no longer wishes to take liquids, but you're required to make him get them down. I found it a huge help to wear a paper nurse's cap.

"The next two suggestions my child thought of himself, so they are right out of the horse's mouth. The first consists of building a theater in miniature. He used an empty carton as a stage, and it was covered with a reasonably good-looking rag. He then arranged scenes in the box, using small plastic furniture, blocks, Christmas-tree ornaments or toys. His actors were those miniature dolls and comic characters from the dime store. He played one of his records for the sound effects and the dolls were supposed to be acting or singing. For a spotlight he used our color-slide projector, but a flashlight would do just as well, or a lamp aimed at the stage.

"The other idea also makes use of cardboard cartons, and those cutout magazine pictures. Now he can paste the pictures into a big box, placed with the open part facing him so that he has three walls, a floor and a roof for his building. A second box sitting on top of the first provides an upstairs.

"If pictures or cars are pasted in the box, toy cars can also be used to go into and out of the garage. If the boxes are to be a house, people can live there and small furniture added. Now he can paste down rugs or paste pictures of windows on the sides of the box.

"A cigar box full of tiny dolls is an excellent toy in sickness and in health. These 'people' are small enough actually to ride in toy trucks, or to fit into block or cardboard buildings, and are very inexpensive. They can march in long parades, have adventures in toy airplanes or fire engines, and ride in some cars of an electric train (the gondola, the dumping car, the hopper, the refrigerator car, or in a boxcar if it has a sliding door). They can be affixed on top of the engine or passenger car with a strip of cellulose tape.

"We were amused to notice some of the wild adventures of a tiny rubber doll whose name was Tiny Baby. Tiny Baby rode in planes alone, jumped off high buildings, ran trains at breakneck speed and did, in fact, anything he pleased. Asked what Tiny's parents thought of his experiences, my small son announced that Tiny Baby *had* no parents, and was allowed to eat whatever he wanted and never go to sleep. I realized that Tiny Baby was a projection of my son's dreams of freedom and I imagine he worked out a lot of frustrations by this means.

"If none of these suggestions pleases you or your child, think how much better it is to be a mother during an era of antibiotics! How was it to face ear infection aboard a covered wagon? We've got a lot to be thankful for."

☙ ☙ ☙

What I envy in Mrs. Irwin is her imagination. I could never embroider a story of my childhood to make it seem worth telling and I can't think of activities for children aside from those I remember loving myself. Boys can spend hours with a collection of miniature cars and there are dozens of fascinatingly realistic ones which can be bought at a good toy store. Sometimes you can find very miniature trains (without motors or tracks) which can be run on a small surface. When one of my sons had to lie on a couch for a month he was happy with a large baking pan of water on the floor in which he arranged docks and sailed the miniature boats which I bought or carved from balsa wood and painted with model-plane colors. Models of planes and trains and boats and cars and scenery can now be bought at model stores in an endless variety of kits, from the simple ones which a six-year-old merely glues together, to those which will keep an adolescent busy for a week.

For boys and girls there are kits for sewing, bead stringing, basket and pot-holder weaving, leatherwork, paper-doll cutting. A construction set, of wood or metal pieces, has dozens of possibilities aside from those in the instruction book, and a boy wants to branch out into his own designs. Doll play can be revived by a few additions to equipment.

The main problem with purchased kits is that if they are beyond a child's capacity, and he cannot adapt them to his level, he will quickly become discouraged. It's always worth remembering that new playthings don't have to be bought at the store. Creation is more soul-satisfying (as well as time-consuming) than the actual play with an object when it is finished. That's why a doll's bed made by the child from a shoe box and equipped with sheets and blankets which she has cut from rags fascinates her more than the finest purchase. A good set of building blocks will challenge a boy to ever more elaborate constructions from the age of two to the age of eight. If a child can't create something new, his second choice is to change something old to a new purpose. This is why, to the distress of his father, he wants to wrench the top off a tin railroad passenger car in order to have it carry real freight.

An invalid's table that extends over the bed is a sound investment for any family.

You don't need to think as far back as covered-wagon days to realize how much convalescence has been shortened and simplified. It was only a little over twenty-five years ago that we had to wait for days, hoping for a favorable crisis, in pneumonia. A child having scarlet fever, even mildly, had to stay in bed for three or four weeks, with good cause. Rheumatic fever required bed rest for many months. Ear infections, which can now usually be stopped in their tracks in a couple of days, used to have to be lanced; and then the doctor and parents would sit with crossed fingers, just hoping that the discharge would cease before too many days and that the infection would not spread to the mastoid bone.

Convalescence was not only long-lasting — it was agonizing.

THE DOCTOR EXAMINES
YOUR CHILD

The competency of a physician
depends on a balance of skills.

《◆

A MOTHER WRITES that she feels dissatisfied with the briefness of
the physical examinations her child receives on routine visits
to the doctor. "What does a good physical examination consist
of, anyway?" she wants to know.

It's a risky business for any one doctor to try to explain medical
practices when there are 200,000 practitioners in the land, each
one of whom will have somewhat different views about each
point. But here goes.

In the first place, a physical examination is only one part of
the process by which a physician makes an evaluation of an
individual. The others are of course the history (the story the
patient or parent tells) and the laboratory tests, if any. I think
it's correct to say that in a majority of medical visits, especially
for checkups, the history of how the patient has been functioning and feeling reveals more information than the physical
examination. Think of the areas that are of most concern to

parent and doctor in infancy: the diet that's offered and how well it is taken; gain in weight and other measurements; advances in motor skills; social responsiveness; bowel function; toilet training, if any; sleep; contentedness versus crying; respiratory or other infections; skin condition; effect of the baby on other members of the family. On only three of these eleven topics is the physical examination apt to shed much light.

In the older child coming in for a routine visit, diet, growth, sleep, infections are still important subjects. In addition there will be questions about adjustment to siblings, parents, friends, school, self. Only in regard to growth and infections does the examination contribute.

Even in regard to growth and infections, the history is as important as the examination in coming to conclusions. The fact that a child is slender or plump in today's examination would leave us almost completely in the dark about its significance unless we knew the past course of his weight curve and his adjustment. Let's take two examples. A child has been somewhat high-strung and thin since infancy. On a percentile chart his weight at many visits has stayed close to the tenth percentile line, meaning that 10 per cent of children his age weighed less than he, 90 per cent of children more than he. Today's examination shows that in the six months since his last examination he has gained more than usual and is now at the twenty-fifth percentile line — 25 per cent of children his age weigh less than he. His mother states that life seems to be going particularly well for him. He is still a somewhat slender child on examination, but his mother and doctor have every reason to be delighted with the state of his health.

An extreme example at the other end of the scale would be a child whose physique looks perfect in today's examination; but his past record shows that he was always overweight before and his mother mentions that he has been drinking and urinating more often than usual in recent weeks. This is a classical story for the onset of diabetes, which can be verified with tests for sugar in the urine and blood.

ⓦ ⓦ ⓦ

Now let's run through the main parts of a physical examination to see how much significance they have in the routine checkups of a baby or of a child.

Since childhood means growth, the weight is an easy, factual way to keep rough tabs on progress, as long as it is interpreted with good judgment. Length or height is always measured, too, and provides a record of one aspect of body build and development. Usually it takes a serious chronic illness or family disturbance to throw a child's length off course.

Many doctors, including myself, don't take the temperature of babies or children who come for routine checkups without symptoms of physical illness. It is seldom elevated under these circumstances, and when it is elevated it usually indicates only the early stages of an ordinary respiratory infection. Rectal temperature taking is felt to be an indignity by most young children. However, other doctors prefer to take temperatures routinely, thinking of the rare case in which an unsuspected fever proves to be a first sign of real trouble.

The first section in a doctor's examination is usually labeled "general appearance," and this includes the child's build, state of nutrition, behavior, and whether he appears healthy or ill. The doctor is gaining impressions about these important aspects all the time he is with the child, without using his hands or any instrument, and is automatically comparing him with other children of the same age. The condition of the skin is seen in a glance.

In infancy the head is measured and the fontanel (the soft spot) is felt, to rule out the possibility of the rare diseases in which the head enlarges too rapidly or slowly.

The lower eyelid is usually pulled down and inspected because pallor of the blood vessels here indicates the possibility of anemia (which is fairly common in the latter half of the first year and in the second year), and the need for a blood count, in order to be sure. The "straightness" or co-ordination of the two eyes is also noted.

In the school-age child it is important that someone give the vision-chart test at least once a year, whether it's the school, the child's regular doctor or the eye specialist. This is particularly important in order to detect nearsightedness, which may develop fairly rapidly at this age, especially if there is nearsightedness in the family, or astigmatism. (When there are severe defects of these two kinds, the teacher or parent is likely to notice the unusual position in which the child holds a book. But milder degrees mays go unnoticed by others, and uncomplained of by the child.)

There are other parts of the eye examination which the general doctor is able to perform: the size and roundness of the pupils; whether they contract when light is shone into them or brought close to them; the appearance of the retina in the back of the eye when examined with the ophthalmoscope light. But these tests are often omitted in the routine periodic examinations of healthy children. They are made with great care when there are any symptoms pointing to disease of the nervous system or eyes. Examination of the retina requires considerable co-operation on the part of the patient, or drops to dilate the pupils.

The nose is briefly inspected with a flashlight, but this usually reveals something only when there is allergy, or a discharge from a cold, sinusitis, or an object which the child has stuffed up there.

The examination of the eardrums is very important in young children when there is or has recently been a cold or sore throat with fever, because they acquire ear infections much more readily than older children and adults. Some doctors, including myself, prefer not to anger or frighten, with an ear examination, the older baby or very young child who is too young to co-operate, when he has been well since the last examination.

The testing of hearing is usually not attempted routinely in the early years because it is very uncertain unless done by an expert. But if there is any doubt, or if a child has had serious ear infections or is slow in developing clear speech, he should be tested by an expert. The child over four or five who is in for a semiannual general checkup may be tested with a watch tick or the whispered voice.

The mouth and throat are always examined to keep track of teeth and tonsils, and to detect mild infections such as thrush, which is fairly common in infancy and interferes with nursing. When there are acute illnesses with fever, the throat is, of course, the place where the seat of the infection is most often found. On the first examination after birth the roof of the mouth is inspected for cleft palate.

In the early months it is noted whether the head is held straight on the neck and can be rotated freely to both sides. In acute illness the doctor flexes the neck to rule out meningeal irritation. The lymph glands in the neck, armpits, groin are felt briefly. The commonest conditions in which they are enlarged are throat, tonsil, skin infections. Occasionally they point to more serious diseases.

The lungs are often percussed (tapped) and listened to, briefly, but when a child is healthy this is mainly a doctor's habit. He would be quite surprised if he heard anything unusual. It's a very different matter when there is a serious cough, which raises questions of bronchitis, pneumonia, asthma; then the lungs are examined painstakingly in all parts.

The heart also may be percussed and listened to briefly. There is little chance that it could have become diseased from one visit to another unless the child has had at least mild symptoms of ill health, such as pallor and fatigability. A good percentage of children have a mild "accidental" heart murmur in the early years, which is of no health significance and which will fade away as they grow older. But the physician wants to keep track of these in his records, in case a question about the heart comes up later.

Blood pressure is taken infrequently in early childhood unless there are symptoms pointing to one of the rare conditions that elevate it. It is difficult to determine blood pressure without co-operation, and the effort bothers young children.

There are several aspects of the abdomen that are routinely checked in infancy. Is there more than the usual amount of gas? How far along toward closing is the umbilical ring? (This is of more importance to the mother than to the doctor.) What's the size of the liver? Is the spleen large enough to be felt below the ribs? Are there any unusual masses?

During the rest of childhood the abdomen is felt briefly, but there is rarely anything to be found except when there are symptoms of local disease such as appendicitis.

In infancy the genitals are examined to see that they are correctly formed — that the boy's testicles are descended and the urinary opening is in the right place. There is no need to go on checking these particular facts — unless, of course, there are symptoms such as burning, discharge, difficulty in urinating.

The baby's arms and legs are observed to see that he uses them freely and that there is good muscle tone. The doctor is on the sharp lookout for signs of orthopedic defects such as dislocation of the hip and any tendency to clubfoot, because early treatment of these is important. In the second year the child is watched for bowlegs, knock-knees, weak ankles, excessive toeing out or in. In later childhood almost any trouble with the legs will be announced by symptoms which the child or parent will report.

The doctor will test a few reflexes during infancy such as the knee jerks, the ankle jerks, the Babinski (the way the toes respond when the sole of the foot is scratched). There is considerable variation in these among healthy babies who are developing normally, so these observations are little more than a formality. The reflexes are more important, and are tested more intensively when there is any question about neurological (brain or nerve) disease. A complete neurological examination could easily take a half hour or more.

☙ ☙ ☙

I think I have said enough to give you a rough idea that there is no definite performance which constitutes "a good physical examination." Its focus varies at successive age periods. The first examination by a new doctor, whether in infancy or later in childhood, has more ground to cover than subsequent routine re-examinations. Any one part of the examination becomes *much* more intensive when there are symptoms of acute or chronic trouble in that part of the body. In a sense, in most visits, the examination is mainly a check on the history.

To be sure, the examination is also intended to assure the patient and the physician that all the major areas of the body have been surveyed, in case there is trouble brewing which has given no signal yet. To a degree this works out. But the degree is very limited. If a doctor were to attempt the ultimate in ruling out any possibility of lurking disturbance at each visit, he would have to take a two-hour history, do a one-hour physical examination, and order several hundred dollars' worth of laboratory tests. If the patient and he could afford this they would still have to make other appointments to go over the findings and then discuss the matters which were actually bothering the patient or parent.

A beginning medical student takes over an hour to perform and write up a routine physical examination on a healthy baby. First he has to stop and think what he is going to do next. Let's say it's the lungs. He recalls the correct order of observations: inspection of the extent, rate, and symmetry of chest expansion; palpation for vocal fremitus (the buzz that is felt by the hand when the patient makes sounds); percussion for resonance; auscultation (with the stethoscope) for the character of the breath sounds and voice sounds, and also for the clicks or wheezes which would denote bronchitis. He then repeats each procedure on every area of the lungs, very deliberately, focusing intently.

The baby's vigorous movements frequently interrupt his progress. The insignificant little noises that babies are always making — coos, snorts, gurgles, burps — sound like a violent thunderstorm through the stethoscope, and raise all kinds of questions in the student's mind. If the baby gets crying, the uproar seems to blot out the sound of the percussion notes, and everything else that might be heard through the stethoscope. He has to pause after each step of the examination to write it down before he forgets.

The experienced physician taps several selected areas, which assures him that the lungs are clear (just as the history suggested) and that the heart is not enlarged. If the baby's screams obliterate the sound, he gets the same message of hollowness through the finger of his left hand which is being tapped. He shifts the stethoscope bell unhesitantly over the same spots and instantly recognizes the characteristic sounds of healthy lungs everywhere. He isn't bothered by — in fact, hardly notices — the much louder sounds of saliva and snorting coming down from the nose and throat. While he's listening he automatically observes the normality of the rate and depth and ease of breathing. The examination of this small pair of lungs has probably taken less than a minute.

The essentials of a monthly examination of a baby who is prospering in all respects could probably be done within five minutes in most cases if the doctor didn't stop to talk and demonstrate to the mother. The before-school examination of an older child, which includes testing of blood pressure, vision, and hearing, would take longer. The examination of a child who was sick with an obvious or obscure disease would take longer still.

So the competency of a physician, and his value to a family, has only a small relationship to the elaborateness or duration of his average physical examination. It depends, rather, on a balance of skills: attentiveness and understanding in hearing the various aspects of the history, relating the symptoms in his own mind to probable and possible disorders (psychological as well as physical), paying particular attention to those aspects of the physical examination that would be most apt to throw light on the diagnosis, but without ignoring other parts of the body, leaving enough time to discuss conclusions.

Since the use of the time of any medical visit involves judicious compromises, and since I believe that mothers are confronted with psychological and developmental questions in their children a hundred times more often than with unsuspected physical disease, I'll express my personal opinion that in a periodic office visit of a child who appears physically healthy the examination should be as brief as is sensible, to allow attention to be given to the real concerns of the parent.

PHYSIQUE, EXERCISE, AND
PHYSICAL FITNESS

Children should develop their muscles and vigor and posture to the degree that is expected by Nature.

❦❦❦❦❦❦❦❦❦❦❦❦❦❦❦❦❦❦❦❦❦❦❦❦❦❦❦❦❦

PARENTS HAVE ALWAYS wanted to know how to foster good physical development in their children.

More recently they've become concerned about "fitness" too, since physical educationists have warned us that American children, whom we have liked to think of as the healthiest in the world, are actually lagging behind the young people of many other countries in their fitness. The readiest explanation is that many of our children aren't getting much exercise any more. In simpler days they walked to school or wherever else they were going. Now they are taken by car or bus. In their free time they used to be actively playing, and they usually preferred to be racing around outdoors because there was so much more freedom and company there. Now television lures the young ones in and sits them down, for an average of twenty hours every week. Some have the regular privilege of sitting all Saturday afternoon in the movies too.

The character of the bony framework inside each of us —
whether heavy- or light-boned, whether broad-shouldered or
slender, whether tall or short, whether pleasingly shaped in the
face — is mainly determined by the genes we happened to inherit
from our various ancestors at the moment we were conceived. A
serious chronic illness or a drastic emotional strain in the family
or a severe restriction of diet may slow down the growth of a
child in height, but only to a moderate extent. Such misfortunes
as these do not touch the great majority of American children.

The size and shape of the muscles that are attached to our
bones are also largely determined by the germ cells which made
each of us. To be sure, the amount of exercise we give to different muscles will influence their size to a degree. The ballet
dancer's calves and thighs are slightly larger because of her hours
of work each day. The eager boy who is exercising with dumb-
bells can increase the circumference of his biceps enough to
measure the difference. But still there are ballerinas and figure
skaters with slender legs. And the stringy youth who hopes to
make his body a solid mass of lumps, like the strong man in the
body-building advertisements, is doomed to disappointment.
Another adolescent who has never made much of an effort in
sport or hard labor may end up with a well-muscled body.

When it comes to the amount of soft tissue ("fat" is such an
ugly word) which is distributed through the different zones of
the body, it is probable that the strongest determining factor
is the genes with which the individual is endowed (or handi-
capped) at conception. Dr. William Sheldon and his colleagues,
who developed the system of body description called somato-
typing, believe they would be able to recognize the bodily proportions of a person who was born with a natural tendency to
be obese even if he were emaciated from starvation at the moment when they happened to measure him. The "endomorphs,"
the people of the extreme type who have the greatest liability
to put on extra fat (in contrast to the extremely heavy-boned,
heavy-muscled people, the "mesomorphs," and the extremely
narrow, slender people, the "ectomorphs") are large and round

in the middle, but have "ham-shaped" limbs which taper down to small hands and feet. Of course most of us are not predominantly one or another type but have some combination of these three tendencies. Men on the average have more of the mesomorph in them and women have more of the endomorph.

But parents and doctors and physical educators have always known that many individuals don't maintain the same amount of fat all their lives. Dr. Sheldon noted that most individuals, whether fat or lean, come as close to ideal as possible at the beginning of adulthood, perhaps because Nature conspires to aid romance. The individual with a tendency to plumpness frequently shows it in the pre-adolescent period, becomes somewhat more slender in adolescence, then begins to put on weight again in the twenties and thirties.

芝 芝 芝

There are certainly environmental and emotional factors which affect a child's state of nutrition. In many parts of the world there are various kinds of malnutrition, because parents can't procure or don't know the right dietary essentials, but there is much less excuse for this in our country.

Probably the commonest type of unnatural thinness in America is caused by a chronic feeding problem. It most frequently starts when the child is going through a phase of picky eating at one or two years of age, or after an illness (see "The Poor Eater," page 151). This creates anxiety and frustration in any mother who is not casual by nature. But the more she frets or cajoles or forces, the more it lowers her child's appetite and increases his obstinacy. It's a vicious circle all right, most prevalent here where food is plentiful and where mothers are conscientious in providing a well-balanced diet.

This kind of feeding problem keeps thousands of American children thinner than they would be otherwise. It is particularly likely to occur in those families in which the mother was

herself a very poor eater in childhood. The worry about sufficient intake gets passed from generation to generation, and
creates the very condition which it is trying to prevent. I mention it first because it shows the futility of trying to improve a
child's physical development by anxious persuasion.

Another type of unnaturally thin child is the one whose
constant nervous tension uses up an excessive amount of energy
(and often holds down appetite at the same time). One such
child is an unhappy worrier, but another may be a cheery
dynamo.

Emotional factors can lead to overfeeding too. Though most
of the children whose mothers are urging food will react with
poor appetite and balkiness, a few submit docilely to stuffing
and become fatter and fatter. You'd think that a mother who
was forcing food because she has a deep anxiety about nutrition
would be able to relax as soon as she saw the child becoming
overweight. But, as the unhappy parent who has this worry
knows, the fear persists, and she may even bring her obese child
to a doctor still complaining that he doesn't eat enough.

Overeating may result from emotional factors in the individual
himself, whether child or adult. There is the person who has
never developed much independence or initiative but, like a
baby, continues to get his main security from eating and being
cared for by others. And there are quite a few people who notice
that whenever life presents disappointments — in friendships or
romance or work — their appetites and their weights go up.
Overweight, however it starts, becomes a vicious circle, because
it creates self-consciousness, restricts social life, increases unhappiness, and thus may lead to greater appetite. Obesity also
decreases exercise and thereby conserves calories.

The different effects of emotional tension on nutrition once
struck me most dramatically in the case of two excessively
rivalrous brothers. The older boy was an unhappy person who
was resentful toward all the other members of his family, had
no friends, withdrew into himself. He was fat. The young one
was sociable, tense, overactive, and insisted on every single privi-

lege the older one had. He was thin. Because the older one was
so miserable at home, it was eventually decided to send him to a
very understanding boarding school. There he made an excellent
adjustment, and in four months, without dieting, he lost twelve
pounds. The thin one became much more relaxed at home and
gained eight pounds in the same period.

Ⓜ Ⓜ Ⓜ

The term "physical fitness" is used by physical educationists
to cover a variety of traits such as strength, endurance, posture,
skill, and grace.

Strength has to be considered in relation to different parts
of the body. A long, lanky individual may have strong legs for
running and jumping and yet be so slender in the arms that he
can barely "chin" himself once. (I feel sympathetic to these
boys, who always get laughed at in a gym class, because I could
never chin myself or do push-ups.) A weight lifter *has* to have
a heavy, well-muscled body to start with, if he is ever to be really
good.

Regular exercise will increase the strength of any set of
muscles to a considerable degree, but it won't change a person
who is muscularly inadequate for some sport into a champion.
And muscles which have acquired additional strength by deliberate exercise will lose part of this as soon as the exercise is
abandoned.

Endurance is even more dependent on exercise than is
strength. Endurance comes partly from the strengthening and
conditioning of the body muscles that are being used in a particular sport or work, and partly from the strengthening of the
heart and breathing muscles that will improve the transportation of oxygen and carbon dioxide. Endurance, too, will
promptly decrease as soon as vigorous exercise is given up.

It's disappointing, isn't it, to realize that strength and endurance will diminish when not being regularly called upon.

But this is only the reverse side of our bodies' marvelous ability to respond to need. They are ingeniously adaptable in so many respects. They adjust to cold climates by learning to conserve heat, to high altitudes by enriching the blood and to low altitudes by thinning it again, to excessive sunshine by tanning the skin and to little sunshine by paling it, to hard use of the palms by laying down calluses which are shed when the work is over. You couldn't design a body that would respond positively to need unless it also responded negatively to lack of need.

What this all means — in terms of strength and endurance — is that there is little permanent gain in going in for vigorous exercise for short periods of time. It's the exercise that a person takes regularly through the week and through his life that maintains his level of fitness.

Most people who take regular exercises claim that they feel better — more bouncy, and at the same time more at peace with the world — and think that they look better. This is my opinion too. But it's hard to be sure about this because human beings are extremely suggestible. Experiments have proved that if a man believes that vaccine will diminish his colds, it will, whether the shots he receives contain bacteria or whether they contain only salt water.

Just what makes for co-ordination and posture and grace is a confusing matter to untangle. I remember well one of the first families for whom I became the pediatrician. The older child, a girl, was graceful from the start. From six months onward she picked up everything so delicately that the parents never had to put breakables out of her reach, and her toys lasted forever. The son in his early years lunged for whatever plaything he sought, grabbed it in his whole fist if he didn't knock it on the floor first, stumbled over something almost every time he crossed a room. Yet he was a happy, undestructive character. When differences like these come out so early in life you suspect that they are inborn, at least in part. But emotional factors complicate the picture.

I think of athletic and graceful people as usually being the secure and outgoing type, but if that's true there are many exceptions. Some withdrawn people subject to the mental disease schizophrenia are unusually graceful. The great ballet dancer, Nijinsky, was a famous example. I remember a college friend who was such a natural athlete that he could become an expert in any sport in a quarter of the time it would take the average devotee, but who on the dance floor shuffled around miserably. One tennis player, when he sees victory in his grasp, does better and better. Another plays well when he is behind and then always goes to pieces when he gets ahead.

Posture is another area in which both the shape you were born with and your feelings about life play a part. The heavy-boned, heavy-muscled mesomorph has a tightly knit body which tends to maintain a good posture. A spindling ectomorph has a spine which readily slumps forward in the neck and in the small of the back, unless he has a proud spirit to buoy him up.

A slouched posture can neatly express a variety of attitudes: self-consciousness, shame, lack of confidence, discouragement, resentment, especially in the individual who can't easily vent his feelings in words. Childhood and adolescence is a period when it's hard to know what one's own feelings are and when it's often risky to express them, so posture is a handy outlet. An energetic mother is constantly bothered by the poor posture of her languid child. She hisses at him "Sit up straight!" twenty times a day. But of course such a child characteristically responds to prodding in a passive, obstinate way. As soon as attention is distracted, he slouches even more, without any conscious realization of it.

As for co-ordination and skill, their most rewarding aspect is that once learned by hard practice — whether it's in ice skating or piano playing or typing — they stay learned. To be sure, a person becomes rusty and he may feel quite discouraged about how much he has forgotten, but actually he can get back to nearly his former level of skill in a very short time compared with the long struggle it took to achieve it in the first place.

This of course speaks in favor of children's learning, when young and adaptable, a sport or skill which they'll enjoy the rest of their lives. If only they had the sense to realize it! Naturally they are full of enthusiasm when they first see an expert perform. They imagine, in their sublime innocence and egotism, that if they could just acquire a tennis racket or ballet costume or violin, they'd soon be performing to the cheers of the audience. Children will stick with great perseverance to acquiring skills which are almost within their power and which everyone else in the neighborhood is practicing (jacks or hoola hoops, for instance) but most of them quickly become discouraged as soon as they sense that real accomplishment is way beyond them. Then when the parent finds himself being more insistent than the child about practice, the latter's enthusiasm turns into rebellion.

🖾 🖾 🖾

It seems as if most of the thoughts I've expressed so far about physical development and fitness have been fatalistic or pessimistic: so much depends on the equipment our children happen to be born with, and parental efforts too often work in reverse. But the outlook is not that hopeless.

We have to accept our children's bony and muscular endowment, because we gave it to them and because we can't change it. But there are two different ways to accept it. One is reluctant. The other is serene. If we are miserable about our son's shortness or our daughter's tallness, we make them feel the same way, whether or not we try to hide our concern. If we show we think they are wonderful as they are, they'll feel good about themselves too.

In regard to fatness or thinness we have to admit that we have only a partial control. We can't make a child eat more, or less, by nagging — we're apt to produce the opposite effect. When a child is thin it's good to check with doctor and teacher to be sure that nothing more needs to be done in investigating health or adjustment.

If a child is only slightly plump in the seven-to-fifteen-year-old period, I think it's wise for parents to keep their mouths shut and their fingers crossed, since so many of these individuals will slim down by themselves later if no fuss is made.

Definite obesity is a much tougher nut to crack. The child faced with such a handicap is inclined to feel that his parents are persecuting him when they try to limit his diet. He should be encouraged to work on the problem with an outsider — a family doctor who inspires confidence, or a psychiatrist, or a supervised weight-reducing group in school. The mother can co-operate mightily by adjusting the family menus, and keeping cakes, cookies, candy out of the house most of the time, so that temptation is minimized.

As for exercise, I myself think that all children should stay outdoors (when it's not raining) at least a couple of hours a day — more when the weather is pleasant and when there is no school — so that they will develop their muscles and vigor and posture to the degree that is expected by Nature. This can be accomplished if the parents believe in it. Then children take it for granted and enjoy it. If they later get the idea from friends that it would be fun to rush to television right after school, the parents only have to make it quite definite that there is no television and no coming indoors till five or five-thirty.

Through P.T.A.'s and other channels parents can campaign for supervised after-school games in playgrounds in the elementary grades, and for sports for all boys who are interested in the high-school years. (I'm not enthusiastic about highly competitive overemphasized athletics for a few individuals, especially before ninth grade.)

I have a prejudice against forcing girls to participate in competitive athletics, particularly after they enter adolescence. Many of them have no appetite for such battles, which were really invented by boys, for boys. But it's fine if they can be offered such activities as group dancing, swimming, tennis, golf, riding, skiing and skating.

Where such luxuries are impossible there are still walking and bicycling — for both sexes — and it's up to parents to see that their children get a reasonable amount of these healthful forms of transportation. (It bothers me to see high-school boys standing on corners trying to thumb rides for a half mile.)

In the final analysis it seems to me that the most important contribution parents make to their children's physical development is to bring them up so that they have confidence in themselves and love life. These attitudes can be counted on, better than other motivations, to keep them active, set their appetites at the right level, make them stand up proudly. And it's the spirit glowing through that makes different shapes attractive. Audrey Hepburn and Marilyn Monroe both have great appeal. Abraham Lincoln's nobility made his very gauntness inspiring.

HOW IMPORTANT IS
FRESH AIR?

*Enthusiasm for fresh air varies
greatly in different parts of the country, and
in different personality types.*

SOME PEOPLE have a great belief in the beneficialness of fresh
air — and the colder the better. Others don't bother about it,
even at a comfortable temperature, and they hate it when it's
cold. It is supposed to have a bearing on health; yet surprisingly
little research has been done on it. The people who have strong
convictions about the value of fresh air have usually got them
from the way they were brought up — the way people get most
of their other convictions. This probably applies to me too.

Fifty years ago fresh air was very much in style, if you can
use the word "style" for a matter that was taken so seriously.
Adults with tuberculosis were sent, if at all possible, to a sana-
torium in the mountains, where they were often kept on open
porches day and night. Children with bone tuberculosis were
sometimes toughened up to the point where they could comfortably play outdoors in winter with almost no clothes on.

My parents had a sleeping porch built which perched on top

of the front veranda, and it gradually filled with small Spocks. In the coldest weather we'd have rubber hot-water bottles to go to bed with, or china "pigs," or aluminum hot-water cans whose sides would gradually sink in as the air in them shrank with the cold.

At the ages of nine and ten I even went to a fresh-air school. A group of parents, many of them connected with the university, persuaded the board of education to equip and provide a teacher for a large tent classroom, which was located in the back yard of a professor. We sat at our desks in winter in thick felt bags which came up to our armpits, our feet in fleece-lined boots, our arms and fingers half immobilized by our sweaters, overcoats, and mittens. Every hour in winter we would troop out to the open platform to do folk dances to limber us up, to the tunes Miss Jocelyn, our teacher, thumped out on the piano in spite of her gloves.

Gradually, as more was learned about the causes and cures of disease, the excessive enthusiasm for fresh air tapered off. I think that the belief in it varies greatly in different parts of the country, and in different personality types. When I practiced pediatrics in New York City in the 1930's, I didn't have to tell mothers that I recommended daily outings. New mothers asked doctors, as a matter of course, how soon the baby could and should go out in his carriage, just as they asked about vitamins and baths. And most of them conscientiously made excursions to the park, not once but twice a day, summer and winter, unless it was raining or snowing, until the children were in school. This seemed as natural to me as it did to the mothers. They learned to dress for comfort and to pick their locations where they would find congenial friends.

When I moved to a part of the Middle West that is cold in winter, I was surprised and rather shocked, as you can imagine, to see no babies being perambulated, to see so very few children outdoors between November and May, except for the few minutes when they were scuttling to school or back.

☙ ☙ ☙

Do we have anything definite to go on regarding the healthfulness of fresh air? Not as much as we'd like. Experiments have shown that the condition which most definitely makes people miserable and inefficient is the combination of high temperature and high humidity, as all of you know who have experienced hot muggy days in summer. Under very extreme conditions it can be dangerous. It was heat and 100 per cent humidity that killed the crowded prisoners in the Black Hole of Calcutta. The system we depend on most in hot weather, to dispel the heat which our bodies are always generating, is the evaporation of perspiration. The higher the humidity of the air, the less rapidly does evaporation occur. So we instinctively take off as many of our clothes as is permitted and we try to find a draft, or to create one with a fan. The draft carries away some of our body heat and it hastens evaporation by removing the air right close to us which we have already saturated. Increased evaporation is one reason why children love to play with sprinklers and hoses in hot weather. You've noticed on a windy day at the beach that you feel colder when you come out of the water than when you were in.

Young children are lucky today in being permitted to wear so little clothing in hot weather. Babies should have the same privilege, but they often don't because people are so apprehensive about their warmth. Mothers who dare to take their babies out in public clothed only in diapers in very hot weather have told me they get scolded occasionally by strangers — not because of the immodesty but because of the supposed danger of chilling! Yet not one would worry at the beach, which is cooler than a city street. Babies down inside carriages in warm weather will have little circulation of air around them and need to be protected from too much sun or clothing. Babies being sun-bathed are absorbing a lot of heat and should be out of the carriage or bassinet so that moving air can get to them.

An opposite problem from high humidity is the excessively dry climate that exists in so many heated houses and apartments. Cold air does not hold as much moisture as warm air. When cold air from outdoors is heated in a furnace, the relative humidity drops sharply. When the inside temperature gets above 72° people who are not accustomed to it notice the discomfort, particularly in the parched feeling in nose and throat.

In a majority of private homes this does not become a problem, either because there is a thermostat or because the house is so leaky that it's hard to get the temperature up so high. Most apartment and office buildings are more efficiently heated and the furnaceman can get the heat up pretty high if he wants to. The more people there are in a building, the more likely there is to be somebody who feels chilly, no matter what the temperature is, and he complains to the superintendent. So the rule that superintendents and furnacemen seem to go by is "Better too hot than too cold." And the more that people become accustomed to excessive heat in buildings, the more they depend on it and demand it. Even the mother in her own house, on a day when she's at low ebb and feels a bit chilly, is tempted to raise the thermostat a couple of degrees. If she doesn't remember to set it back, she gets used to that temperature and the next time she feels chilly she nudges the thermostat up still higher.

The doctor sees the value of sufficient moisture in the air, during the heating season, in the prompt improvement of so many coughs and croups and stuffed-up noses when he prescribes the use of an efficient vaporizer during infections.

Even in the absence of nose colds, some babies in homes and hospitals become so obstructed by dried mucus in the nasal passages, during the heating season, that they have real difficulty breathing. (They don't know enough yet to breathe through their mouths at such a time.)

The passages of the nose and throat and bronchial tubes contain glands which put out enough mucus to keep the passages comfortably moist at ordinary humidities. The cells lining the passages have "cilia" projecting from them, microscopic oarlike processes which are constantly propelling the mucus, dust, bacteria, and any products of inflammation upward and outward. That's why mucus normally collects in the fronts of our noses and why during a bronchitis the excessive mucus works up from our smaller tubes into our main windpipe, from which we cough it out. When these passages become dried out, this cleaning and protecting system doesn't work well.

Experiments have shown that some of the bacteria that cause sore throats and pneumonia die off much more rapidly in air that is moderately humid than in air that is very dry or very humid. In some parts of the eastern slopes of the Rocky Mountains, where the air is unusually dry to start with and bone dry when it is heated, people are very susceptible to such infections.

Many people who have dandruff will notice that it begins each winter when the heating system gets going full blast, which suggests that an excessive dryness of the air plays hob with the scalp too.

Putting pans of water on radiators has been shown to be ineffective in raising the humidity of a room — it produces only a small fraction of the moisture which is needed. The only practical method for keeping a reasonable humidity in a heated house (short of elaborate air conditioning, or the use of a vaporizer during illness) is to keep the house temperature below 72°.

People sometimes worry whether there will be enough oxygen to breathe in a room that is very crowded, and whether the "stuffiness" (by which they usually mean body odor) in an insufficiently ventilated classroom or bedroom is unhealthy.

There are definite answers to these questions. There is enough circulation of air into any ordinary room to provide plenty of oxygen for everyone it will hold. The stuffiness of a room which comes from too many warm people and too little fresh air has no harmful effect in itself (though, again, high humidity would make for discomfort). In fact, you don't even notice stuffiness after you've been in a room for a minute.

☙ ☙ ☙

Now we should get back to the question of the value of fresh air in the sense of exposure to cold air in winter. I was poking fun at the fanatical belief in it that existed fifty years ago. It was almost a matter of morals or of strength of character. The same attitude is expressed still by the occasional individual (always a man, as far as I know) who prides himself on walking to work without an overcoat, even in zero weather.

No scientific data has been collected, as far as I know, on the value of exposure to cold air. You can't really come to any conclusions on the basis of the statements of believers. People who firmly believe that something will make them feel better — whether it's cold showers or nine hours of sleep or vitamin pills — *will* feel better. It has even been shown in an elaborate experiment with cold vaccine that those subjects who volunteered to take vaccine but who got injections of salt water instead, without knowing it, reported that the total duration of their colds was diminished by 75 per cent — just as in the case of those who received vaccine.

But I do think there are hints, if you want to believe them (and you can see that I do), that reasonable exposure to cold air is at least mildly beneficial. The lumberjack, the regular skier, the man who walks to work has a toned-up temperature-regulating mechanism which in winter conserves his body heat and protects him against chilling in all but extreme situations. The person who remains almost constantly in a warm house is easily chilled on occasional exposure, unless he has just exactly the right amount of clothing on him. Since babies and children do have to go out occasionally and since chilling is thought to play a part in starting certain infections, there may be some protection in regular outings.

Certainly babies and children and adults who get out regularly in winter have redder cheeks, and the baby who lives always in a too hot home has a distinctly "pasty" complexion. I don't know whether the healthfulness of pink cheeks is more than skin deep, but they look wonderful.

Children and adults who get out for exercise — in any temperature — have better appetites. Hundreds of mothers have complained to me how bored and irritable their young children are when they have to be kept indoors in winter because of colds, and how much more pleasant home life immediately becomes when they are at last allowed to run off their energy outside.

I think it's fun and helpful for babies to get used to other scenes than the four walls of home, and they certainly love being perambulated or even lying in the carriage in the yard, watching the branches wave. (However, if a baby sleeps in a room that's cold, he'll get his pink cheeks and good appetite anyway.) I think, also, that it is a tonic for many mothers, especially in those preoccupied early months, to have to get out of the house for a while every day, stretch their legs and lungs, see friends and strangers.

☙ ☙ ☙

There is one other point about outings — the clothes. There is an almost irresistible compulsion to overdress babies. The doctor sees them coming to his office in heated cars, encased in layers of sweaters, sacks, coats, shawls, blankets, bags. They are sometimes in a sweat and they occasionally have heat rash in the middle of winter. I'm sure that Nature has endowed each of us with at least a little excessive anxiety about keeping a baby warm and giving him enough to eat. I suppose that through the ages Nature has realized that there are some fairly immature, irresponsible types who have babies, and that the first essential in keeping babies alive until they can begin to make their wants known is a bit of concern on the part of mothers about warmth and food. The trouble is that the conscientious young mothers who need this prompting least are the ones who feel it most sharply.

On the other hand, there's an occasional mother, out to prove her freedom from convention and to prove her baby's hardiness, who puts so little covering on him that it horrifies the grand-parents and the neighbors.

A baby's hands and feet will normally be cool except in hot weather, so this is no sign that he needs more covering. He needs, if anything, less than an older child or adult. If he becomes too cold he'll show it — like anyone else — by com-plaining and by losing his color.

Children old enough to run around are much less likely to be overdressed, I suppose because they look able to take care of themselves. I think quite a few children are underdressed in winter in this day of the snow suit. The fact that a garment is called a snow suit doesn't make it necessarily warm. Those with a good lining of wool or some other insulating material are very satisfactory for cold climates — much handier for child and parent than the stiff overcoat and separate leggings of an earlier day. But I feel shivery myself when I see a small child who has turned blue with the cold in a so-called snow suit that has only a cotton-flannel lining. Of course a suit of this type may be quite adequate for a less severe climate.

HOW MUCH SLEEP
IS ENOUGH?

I myself would always err on the side
of encouraging a little more than average
sleep rather than a little less.

How MUCH SLEEP should a child have? I used to think, when I started to practice medicine, that the answer was definite and easy. Most textbooks of pediatrics, and child-care books for parents, gave some kind of table. One, for instance, would say that the average child needs and will probably get 16 to 20 hours of sleep in the early months, 14 to 16 hours by one year of age, 14 hours by two years of age, 12 hours at six, 11 hours at nine, 10 hours at twelve (to bed at 9 if up at 7).

But the more experience I had the more difficult it became for me to be definite. There are so many factors that influence sleep.

There's a lot of variation in the amount that different babies sleep in the early weeks. Some would say that this only proves that one individual naturally requires much less sleep than another. But I'm not at all sure that innate differences play the largest part in the first month or two. This is the age for colic and for what I call irritable crying (misery for long spells, especially in the evening) and for intermittent fretfulness. It's the age when a few babies stay awake all day and others stay awake half the night, without being particularly unhappy. But in most of these cases the impaired sleep pattern proves not to be permanent. If they are sensibly guided, a majority of these babies are sleeping an average amount by the time they are three months old.

Still, there are a few infants who have no misery and no bizarre pattern who merely sleep considerably less than average, and who go on through childhood with the same tendency. So there may be such a thing as an inherent, inborn sleep pattern, which is different for each individual. If there is, it wouldn't necessarily mean that the child who sleeps less has less need of sleep, but rather that he has a more wakeful — perhaps tenser — nature which simply doesn't allow him to sleep the average amount; his system adapts to this and makes the best of the sleep he does get. Perhaps I'm splitting hairs about this point, but I'm doing so for a purpose. I think that some parents, who happen not to take sleep very seriously, simply state that their children are the kind who need little sleep, and they let it go at that. Yet it might be that with wise guidance these same children could be led to take more sleep and profit by it.

There's not much doubt that children and adults can be accustomed, over a period of time, to take somewhat more or somewhat less sleep than they previously had. For example, during a trip or visit it may be almost impossible to keep children to their usual bedtime. They yawn a lot the first few days and then they seem gradually to adjust, at least to a degree. Adults on a restful vacation (probably without children) may find themselves sleeping a couple of hours longer than they ever thought they could.

A number of years ago I was impressed with an extreme example of how older children can be trained to sleep more. It was at a convalescent hospital for children who had had rheumatic fever with heart disease. In those days there were none of the wonder drugs with which attacks of rheumatic fever can be cut short. The only known treatment was rest. In that hospital the rest regimen was carried out vigorously and the discipline was strict. There were children between the ages of five and eighteen. Even the eighteen-year-olds had to go to bed early (with lights out), and in addition had to take a two-hour nap after lunch, during which no talking, reading, or other distraction was allowed. I was amazed to learn that even adolescents, after being in the hospital a few weeks, went to sleep after lunch and early in the evening — just as two- and three-year-olds do.

Though it may be true that children can get used to somewhat less than the average amount of sleep, without visible harm, this adaptation has limits. For instance there are those sleep problems in the first year of life in which the infant either learns to fight off being put to bed at night (so that instead of settling down at 7 P.M. he insists on being walked till 11 or 12) or wakes two or three times a night and demands company for a total of three to five hours. Most mothers report that these babies do not make up for the lost sleep in daytime naps and are tired and irritable all day long. (The treatment of these problems, which takes only two or three nights, is for the mother to put the baby to bed at a sensible hour and not go back to him at all.) Teachers sometimes have the problem of the child who, month after month, yawns through school and who is found on investigation to be staying up a good part of the night because of family disorganization or neglect.

There are various emotional tensions that are known to interfere with sleep. In a later chapter (page 164), I will be dealing with separation anxiety and the particular bedtime problems of many children around the age of two. But at all stages of childhood, sleep may be impaired by daytime worries, fear of nightmares, guiltiness about undiscovered misdeeds, exaggerated rivalries. These have their deep as well as surface causes. When they persist, they call for the help of the child-guidance clinic or the family social agency.

᛭ ᛭ ᛭

I think that probably the most influential factor of all in the amount of sleep children get is the sleep pattern in which the parents themselves were brought up. Parents tend in most instances to apply the same rules to their children as were applied to them. (A few, in revolt, swing to the opposite extreme.)

I was brought up in an Eastern city by very conscientious parents who themselves had been put early to bed in childhood, and who took rules of health for children very seriously. When I was eight or nine years of age I and my sisters were still having our supper of cereal, fruit, and cocoa at a children's table at 5:30 P.M., stayed indoors afterward, and were expected to be in bed by 7 P.M., when our parents started their dinner. (I can still remember the indistinct rumbling sounds of my father's voice and the higher-pitched murmurs of my mother's voice which came up through the ceiling to the second floor.) They not only believed that growing children needed a lot of sleep. They assumed, too, that parents were entitled to a quiet dinner by candlelight. It wasn't until each of us was about twelve that he was privileged to graduate to the dinner table and its grown-up meal.

When I started to practice pediatrics in New York City twenty years later, I still assumed (since I hadn't seen anything different) that all young children who are carefully brought up have cereal and fruit at 5:30 and are in bed by 7. And as a matter of fact, most of the parents whom I advised went on the same assumption.

Fifteen years later I moved to a different part of the country where a majority of the parents had quite different ideas about supper and bedtime. Children had early supper with their parents. Younger children generally went to bed earlier than older children, but there were surprising variations at each age.

Some of the preschoolers were in bed by 7. But there were plenty who stayed up until 8 or 9 and there were at least a few who didn't turn in until 10 or even later. I was shocked at first. I expected that even the moderately late retirers would have circles under their eyes and would be fatigued and yawning all day. Yet most of those who didn't stay up excessively late looked reasonably healthy.

᭙ ᭙ ᭙

Some parents who believe in the importance of plenty of sleep have a lot more trouble than others in getting their children to bed. We are apt to assume that we put our children to bed in a matter-of-fact manner simply because we know they need their sleep. But under the surface, all kinds of attitudes get mixed into bedtime. One trouble with evening is that the mother as well as the child is tired. If he has been bedeviling her all day, she will probably have accumulated considerable irritation. She can let this out very neatly in the summons to bed. Her tone says, "Now I can legitimately get even with you at last. I'm going to make you stop doing the things you want to do and do what you like least." This tone, if used regularly, can turn a child who loves going to bed into one who fights it, within a couple of weeks.

Or there is the mother who feels chronic irritation but is guilty enough about it so that she lacks masterfulness. She retreats if the child protests vigorously. "You should have been in bed half an hour ago — hurry up," she says crossly. The child, who has become a shrewd lawyer as a result of learning his mother's weaknesses, immediately argues, "Last Saturday you let me stay up till nine," or "You haven't read me a story," or "I want to wait until daddy comes home." The mother wonders if she has been hasty or unfair. Whether she decides to stand firm or to compromise, she hesitates long enough to encourage him to try again the next time. When this kind of arguing has gone on for months, it can easily use up an hour of supposed sleep time every evening.

Of course it isn't that one parent is always masterful about bedtime and another is always unsuccessful. We all have our ups and downs, depending on how we're getting along with the child in other respects and how life is treating us. Occasional lapses don't ruin our discipline. Still, it does take reasonable consistency and a basic friendliness to keep bedtime smooth.

When we're talking about children getting enough sleep — and parents getting enough rest — we shouldn't lose sight of the hour of waking. Here is a situation where I think that early training pays dividends. In some families, one of the parents, at least, has to be up from 6 A.M., simply because the children are wide awake and demanding attention by that hour. In another family everyone is still snoozing when the alarm clock goes off at 8 A.M. What makes the difference? In some cases it may be ascribed to an innate wakefulness which has been apparent since early infancy, or at least wakefulness in one child, who rouses the others. But more often I suspect that training plays the major role, especially the training of the first child. In the early months, a great majority of infants wake between 5 and 6 A.M. whether it's summer or winter, whether the room is dark or light. After four or six months of age most of them show a gradual tendency to sleep later. But if the mother is a highly conscientious person who sleeps with one ear cocked and who leaps out of bed at the first peep or murmur from the baby's room, she may always get to him before he's half awake. This trains him to continue to wake early and to expect attention from the very first moment. But if a mother will play possum in the early dawn, waiting to see whether the baby will go back to sleep or, if he doesn't do that, whether he will at least be content for a while playing with his hands or a toy, the chances are that she will be surprised and delighted with the progress.

If the first child is trained to sleep until a convenient hour, there should be a good likelihood of inculcating the same pattern in subsequent children, even though they have to share rooms.

While we are on training, it's worth mentioning that a majority of babies can be taught to sleep through the usual kinds of household noise, even without a closed door in between: the telephone, television, the calls of older children, the laughs of adult guests in the evenings. On the other hand, if the household tiptoes and whispers near the baby's room, he is being trained to waken whenever a noise is made by mistake. Not all babies can be trained at the same speed to tolerate noise. Some of them are relatively insensitive from the start. At the opposite extreme are those who for the first few weeks will almost jump out of their skins if an object is dropped or a door is slammed. But even the most sensitive ones will gradually tolerate more noise if they are given a chance to learn.

🐦 🐦 🐦

Have I confused rather than clarified the question of how much sleep? I think I have made it clear that there can be no single answer. The amount of sleep a child gets or seems to need is influenced by such factors as inborn differences (which haven't really been proved), the special sleep disturbances of the first couple of months of infancy, the parents' ideas of what is right, the tactfulness and firmness with which the parents get the child to bed, tensions which may keep him wakeful.

Though I think individual factors have to be taken into account by the parents, I don't think that bedtime should be left to a child to decide. I myself would always err on the side of encouraging a little more than average sleep rather than a little less. I suppose that's due to my upbringing, and the fact that doctors usually are conservative, and my general impression that children brought up by careful parents are healthier on the average. After a baby is three months old, I as a parent would aim for the kind of schedule I mentioned in the beginning of this chapter (including a nap until four or five years of age). If my child was getting much less than that, I'd want to discuss with my physician whether this was a peculiarity of no significance or whether it was due to my management. I certainly am not advocating that a mother make her child and herself miserable by insisting on an arbitrary sleep schedule which doesn't fit him — that does more harm than good. I am only suggesting that, in many of the cases in which the sleep is inadequate, there are tensions in the child or blind spots in the parents which could be remedied if tackled in time. It's in infancy that sleep patterns can be more easily modified by parental guidance. The patterns that come out of infancy tend to persist.

SWEETS AND
THE TEETH

Better to keep sweets away as
long and as much as possible.

WHEN I WORKED at the Arsenal Health Center in Pittsburgh, another member of the staff was Dr. Milton Nicholson, a forward-looking professor of dentistry who is intensely interested in preventive dentistry. He and I were always commiserating with each other on our failure to convince any parents — as far as we could see — that it's better to keep candy, soda pop, cookies and such sweets away from children as long and as much as possible.

You can't keep sweets away forever, because children, as they grow older, go to parties and they go to school past candy stores. By then, good parents, even though they limit sweets a lot, have to allow them sometimes because they don't want to act like Old Scrooges.

Why were Doctor Nicholson and I fussing, anyway? There is a great deal of evidence that starches and sugar are the principal cause of caries or decay of the teeth. Researchers believe that the actual holes are dissolved out of the teeth by lactic acid. The lactic acid is manufactured by bacteria that live exclusively on starch and sugar. The studies emphasize that it's the length of time the carbohydrates are in contact with the teeth — hour after hour, year in and year out — that probably counts most. So lollipops are probably worse than candy which dissolves quickly.

Crackers and cookies that get packed into the crevices of the teeth and stuck to the sides are probably worse than semiliquid foods. The carbohydrates in five meals a day are harder on the teeth than in three meals, and constant nibbling a good part of the day is the worst of all. Foods that contain a lot of roughage, like raw fruits and vegetables and firm meats, clean off the teeth to some degree. A drink of water or milk at the end of a meal washes the teeth to some extent and tooth brushing after every meal and before going to bed is best of all.

Most of us parents know these facts in a general way and yet most of us don't seem to pay much attention to them (in my family, too). We aren't careless about our children's health in other respects. We call the doctor for illnesses, take our children for inoculations, give them expensive vitamins to grow strong bones.

The best explanation I can figure out is that there's a very close connection in our minds and hearts between sweets and love. When we were children our parents often showed approval or affection for us with something sweet. "You ate all your vegetables, so you can have a big piece of cake" . . . "You were such a good boy while mother was downtown, you can have a piece of candy" . . . "Mother was proud of how brave you were at the doctor's [or even at the dentist's!]. We'll stop at the soda fountain on the way home." The doctor, who of all people should set a good example, may reward the child who behaves well in his office with a lollipop.

So the feeling — that sweets mean love — is implanted in us early in childhood. It gets built into us deep and strong. Later, the young man gives his girl a heart-shaped box of candy on

Valentine's Day. A grown woman feeling lonely and unappreciated may be able to comfort herself a great deal by buying herself and eating entirely a large box of chocolates. Two of our fondest endearments are "sweetie" and "honey."

When we come to have children of our own we can't easily brush aside this deeply ingrained attitude. We have an overpowering desire to show affection to them the way it was shown to us. We may hear in our ears the words our dentist or doctor or an article explains that sweets harm teeth, but the words don't get through to what you might call the heart.

In other words, Doctor Nicholson and I and all the other professional people who are trying to stem the sirupy tide are up against powerful forces. We are like hunters trying to stop elephants with air rifles.

☙ ☙ ☙

Is it possible to be a kindly mother who humors her children's between-meal cravings and still doesn't sacrifice their teeth to the lactic-acid bacteria?

From infancy onward you can serve them desserts of stewed fruits that are not oversweetened, and raw fruits. You can keep them ignorant of cookies and cakes for a long time, and even after that you can avoid tempting them by simply not having such foods around the kitchen — *if* the adults don't demand them.

You can keep candy out of the house except on a few special occasions. I'd forbid my child to buy candy or other sweets *regularly* coming home from school (or any other time). Above all, you can avoid using candy or sweet desserts as a reward or bribe, which only increases the child's craving for them.

If a child doesn't seem to need a midmorning or afternoon snack, it's better for his teeth to leave it out. If he has to have something, the least harmful for the teeth are probably milk, fruit, vegetable juice, or fruit juice.

⚑ ⚑ ⚑

Although little is known as yet about exactly which nutritional elements will make teeth which are resistant to caries, it has been shown conclusively that the right amount of fluoride in the water consumed by pregnant women and young children is of great value. It will cut down, *by two thirds*, the amount of tooth decay in children who have grown up, from conception, using such water. (The fluoride has to get into the crowns of the baby teeth while they are being formed, which is before birth.) The benefits don't come just to conscientious families but to everybody growing up in a community with fluoridated water.

Fluoridation of the water supply has spread rapidly in recent years, but it still has a long way to go. When it is being considered for the first time in any city, the people want to be assured that it is safe, and this takes some time and discussion. Of course, fluoridation was thoroughly experimented with and proved safe to the satisfaction of medical, dental, and health authorities before it was ever recommended. In fact, fluoride has always occurred naturally in some water supplies — that's how its value was first discovered. I'm proud to have lived in recent years in cities which have had the good sense to give their children this protection. If the proposal comes up in your community, support it by all means.

For the benefit of those children who did not receive fluoride while their teeth were being formed, the dentist can paint the teeth with stannous fluoride. The same substance is now incorporated in a toothpaste which has value if used very regularly.

To give our children the real benefit from tooth brushing, we must instill the habit of doing it after every meal as well as on arising and at bedtime. Remember that decay occurs principally in the hour or two after eating starches and sweets.

II

A Child's Position in the Family

:◇◖◇◖◇◖◇◖◇◖◇◖◇◖

OLDEST, MIDDLE, AND
YOUNGEST CHILD

Though position in the family is important,
it's even more important what kind of family
it is, in spirit, in attitude.

WHEN I LOOKED through the articles that have been published
by psychologists, sociologists, psychiatrists to see what factual
data have been collected about how a child's position in the
family affects his character, I was at first surprised. There is very
little in the way of statistics to show that the oldest turns out
one way and the youngest turns out another way. What statistics
there are indicate that in general there are no great, consistent
differences between oldest, middle, and youngest child as far as
personality or type of difficulty is concerned.

You probably feel like saying, "Nonsense! I *know* that I and
each of my brothers and sisters were strongly influenced by being
first or second or youngest, and I've known similar situations in
other families." I agree. That's why I want to discuss this
topic. There are, of course, several very different ways a first
child, for instance, can turn out, depending on whether he's boy
or girl, large or small, energetic or quiet. The statistics only

show that when you add together the different kinds of first children and compare the average with the average of the different kinds of middle children, the special types we're all familiar with get canceled out or lost in the statistics.

Years ago the staff of the Sarah Lawrence College Nursery School, of which I was a part-time member, were discussing a number of first-born children who had been very upset when the next younger sister or brother was born. Several of these children had changed at least temporarily from gay, friendly eager beavers to quiet, sad mopers. We on the staff were sympathizing with first children in general, because we had the impression that most of them found it tough to be displaced from the only-child position. Then one member of the staff went over the records of all the first children in that school, for several years back, to see how they actually added up. Much to our surprise, the informal statistics showed that for every one who had been distinctly upset at the arrival of the next baby, there was another child who had taken the new arrival completely in his stride and had gone on being just as happy as before.

It may be that these children who breeze through the arrival of the second so successfully are able to do so because of a very special kind of security — just from being first.

Incidentally, a first child is rarely upset by the birth of a third. He or she has apparently experienced whatever jealousy he is capable of with the birth of the second and has been somehow purged in adjusting to it. In fact, most parents are amazed at how fond the first child is of the third, even though he may have shown intense jealousy of the second. It is as if he were now able to feel like a fond parent rather than as a rival. This pattern is the most dramatic evidence that a phase of jealousy — if it is not too overwhelming and if it is gradually digested — may be a truly constructive experience for a child, inoculating him and fortifying him, as it were, against future threats of the same sort.

Though a child's position in the family is important, it's even more important what kind of family it is, in spirit, in attitude. If it's an easygoing family in which the parents just naturally take each child as he comes, then there is more chance that each child will feel comfortable in his particular spot, whichever it is. Most of us parents, though, are more critical of our children than that, show as much disapproval as approval and tend to compare one child with another, in words or in action. Then the children will be more likely to be rivalrous, too, very aware of who's oldest or smartest or strongest or most privileged or successful.

Some parents find it easier to get along with the kind of child who has been quiet and compliant since birth. Others really enjoy spunky children most. Some crave boys, at least at a certain stage in the growth of the family, others crave girls. You can see that these responses of mothers and fathers can be more important in shaping a child's personality than whether he is first, second, or third.

A somewhat related matter is the size of the family. In a general way, the larger the family, the less each child who is born into it will upset the previous balance. Since the parents' interest is divided between more children, there is more chance for each individual to develop in his own natural pattern. At the other end of the scale are the parents who find that they can have only one or two children, or the parents who decide ahead of time that they will have only that number. Then there's often a greater tendency to concentrate their attention, their expectations, and their apprehensions on these one or two.

☙ ☙ ☙

We human beings, if we are reasonably normal, are so constituted that we see our child — and especially the first — not so much as a new, separate, unknown individual but as an expression of ourselves. Oh, of course, we think of ourselves as very enlightened moderns and make pious statements about wanting him to develop in his own way and carve out the life he chooses, as long as he's happy. We are sincere when we say it, and we'll try. But the real we, the human nature that is so strong inside us, usually has no intention of being quite that wishy-washy and permissive. In fact, we sometimes don't wait until a child is born to begin to shape him into the character we envision. A few people who have been in psychiatric treatment while expecting a baby have been surprised to learn, from looking at their dreams and their daydreams, how definitely they are anticipating the special characteristics of the baby who is still entirely unknown, even in respect to his sex.

Generally speaking, we tend to want our child to look something like us but maybe a little more handsome, to enjoy much the same interests or hobbies, to think the same things are funny or inspiring, to do well in one of the careers that we have admired.

And it isn't just the positive things we're concerned about. We dread that our child will be weak or naughty in one of the areas in which we used to be considered weak or naughty, or unsuccessful in some field in which we felt we came close to failure.

Such parental preoccupations aren't necessarily detrimental to children. To be sure, if a father works himself into a lather about whether his son will get into his college and fraternity, it may affect badly a boy who is not cut out for it. It may exhaust a girl if her ambitious mother is insisting on dancing lessons *and* music lessons *and* skating lessons. But the hopes of sensible parents who don't push too hard can be influential in creating characteristics that are really valuable to the child and the world.

I have been talking as though the parents always focused on the first child, identified him with themselves, and left their imprint strongly on him. Of course this isn't necessarily true. Plenty of parents are reasonably casual with their first and some parents do their concentrating on a second or third child. This sometimes happens, for instance, when they have been waiting impatiently for a girl after having had two or three boys. The girl who eventually appears may receive a greater amount of attention and end up with a character that is more like that of some first or only child.

⚑ ⚑ ⚑

In lots of families, to be the middle child or one of the middle children looks like the most comfortable position of all. The parents have learned a lot of lessons the hard way with the first. They're now apt to be more sure of themselves, more relaxed. So many mothers have exclaimed to me, in almost the same words, "The second is so *easy!* I don't seem to worry about him. I don't even have to wonder what to do. I just find myself doing what's necessary and it usually turns out to be right. Why, I don't even have to stop to ask myself whether I should punish him or overlook his naughtiness. If I do punish him it always clears the air — I don't feel guilty about it and he cheers up soon afterward. Sometimes my husband and I wonder if we're neglecting him — we fuss over him so little. But if it *is* neglect he seems to thrive on it. He keeps himself busy and happy most of the time. But when he does want a little company he's so appealing that no one can resist him, even strangers on the street. He enjoys being hugged, which is so different from the first."

Of course not all second children get off to such a smooth start. The mothers who talk this way are emphasizing one side of the picture. This kind of relaxation on the parent's part is apt to protect a child's character from overdependence on the mother, or on other people later in life. He can usually make his own way without much stewing about it.

Children who are second or later in the family are more apt than the first to learn early how to get along with other children — both positively and negatively. They catch the fun of rough and tumble when this comes naturally at one and two and three and four. (The first or only child, if he has few chances to be with other children in the early years, usually finds them pretty strange, thoughtless, and violent compared with the polite grown-ups he's used to.) The second or later child in most families discovers how to defend himself without much delay. If he has an older brother who picks on him he may wince and cry at nine months or twelve months, but by eighteen months he will probably be able to hang on to his possessions like grim death and fight back like a tiger. It's amazing how often a younger child may eventually get the upper hand of one who is considerably older, bigger, and stronger. Probably the main reason he can fight more boldly is that he doesn't feel the guilt which the older child has usually been taught to feel about meanness toward the baby.

But life can be tough for a second child too: A frequent source of tension — especially if there are only two children and they are both boys or both girls — may be a constant excessive striving of the second to keep up with the first: to *always* climb a tree if he climbs a tree, to get a new hat if he gets a new hat, to stay up as late, to play with his brother's friends even if he has to neglect his own. This intense rivalry may or may not make the younger one miserable. More often he remains a cheerful person through all his striving, though it may keep him thin and high-strung, and it may irritate his older brother a lot. Occasionally this kind of ambitiousness produces very strong leadership qualities in the second child among his own group, usually of a constructive type. A couple of times I have seen a second child who was ingenious in leading his older brother or another child into trouble. In later life an exaggerated rivalry may influence a younger girl, for instance, to become engaged, get married, have children just as soon as her sister does, or influence a boy to choose the same career as his older brother even though they have quite different personalities. Whether the results will be good or not will depend on whether the competitiveness is so powerful that it is blinding or whether it is balanced by ordinary amounts of judgment.

Though a majority of second children make a good adjustment not only to the first but to a third in the family, an occasional one seems to get into a real squeeze. He becomes pessimistic about ever being able to catch up to the first (there are few ways in childhood that a second ever *can* pass the first, but that doesn't discourage most of them). Then when the third child is born, the second feels assailed from that direction too. He may stop trying to be more grown up, lose most of his initiative, ask for a lot of help and even relapse into baby talk, thumb-sucking and bed-wetting. When these are temporary reactions to the arrival of the third baby they aren't very serious, but if they persist they show that the middle child is in a tough spot and needs a lot of help, from parents or from professional people. Sometimes the explanation is that the middle child is at a distinct disadvantage, compared with the older *and* the younger, in size or strength or good looks or in physical health. This outcome has been seen, too, when the parents had had two girls, were impatiently waiting for a boy, and greeted a male third child with an overenthusiasm that no amount of tact could conceal from the second girl.

☙ ☙ ☙

About the youngest child in the family, there's lots of variation. The Biblical story of Joseph who was his father's favorite, who was resented by his brothers, and who succeeded in the end is typical of other stories and myths which show how interested mankind has been in the fate of the youngest. It's true about youngest children as about middle children that the majority show no outstanding traits as a result of their position in the family. But among a smaller number two rather opposite trends are often noticed: on the one hand the striving to catch up and excel and, on the other, the willingness to continue to be the baby.

There is a natural enough tendency in most parents to relax progressively in their discipline as they become older and as subsequent children arrive. They've come to realize more and more that children grow and mature largely through their own instincts and through emulation of the parents and that not too much interference is necessary. They also are getting at least a little bit tired. If it is then apparent that this is probably their last child there is also the very human wish to enjoy his childhood as long as possible. These factors added together often mean that fewer demands are made on the youngest. Sometimes his more babyish moments and more babyish attitudes are humored — way beyond what the parents would have put up with in their older children — or even encouraged. It's hard for a person of any age not to become somewhat dependent, self-centered, and demanding under such pampering. And when this indulgence irritates the older brothers and sisters, it may not shame the youngest out of wanting his special privileges; instead, he may give up trying to be acceptable to them and make a greater play for the parents' attention. These are some of the steps that turn a few youngest children into somewhat spoiled creatures, unwilling to work very hard for themselves or anyone else. One interesting medical study of a group of individuals who became chronic invalids, partly through not trying very hard to get well, showed that a disproportionately large percentage of them had been youngest children.

On the other hand the great fondness and uncriticalness of the parents (if it isn't coupled with too much babying) may give the youngest an ideal self-confidence which enables him to use all his capacities to the full. Then if he has also developed considerable competitiveness in the wish to catch up with all his older brothers and sisters, the combination may produce an unusually ambitious and successful person in the work of the world.

❦❦❦❦❦❦❦❦❦❦❦❦❦❦❦❦❦❦❦❦❦❦❦❦❦❦❦❦❦❦❦❦❦❦❦

THE FIRST CHILD'S
SPECIAL POSITION

Our first child
is ourselves.

❦❦❦❦❦❦❦❦❦❦❦❦❦❦❦❦❦❦❦❦❦❦❦❦❦❦❦❦❦❦❦❦❦❦❦

❦ DISADVANTAGES AND ADVANTAGES

I WANT to discuss certain character traits that quite a few parents see in their first child and guiltily reproach themselves for. Here is a composite of the complaints and confessions that I've heard dozens of times: "Our first child is not as happy as he should be. He's rather shy and timid with strange children and with the rougher boys in the neighborhood. On the other hand, he can be quite bossy with younger children. He has friends but he sometimes antagonizes them by being selfish about his playthings, or too insistent in having the play go his way. Yet it hurts his feelings badly when they turn their backs on him after an argument. Of course he blames them. He wants the attention of grownups, too, but he often fails to get it in a winning way. If they don't notice him he's apt to act grumpy or rude. He's doing average work in second grade, but his teacher says that he daydreams too much and that he's not working up to his capacity. At home he's been quite jealous of his next younger sister. He was mean to her at first and has never wanted her to play with his things.

"I've never had the confidence I knew how to manage him, and yet in a way I feel I understand him best of all the children. Perhaps we're too much the same. I didn't know anything about taking care of a baby when I had him and I was insecure. I had to look at the book or call the doctor on the slightest occasion. He fussed a lot the first three months, which didn't get us off to a good start. He never wanted to be cuddled. In the second year I found him hard to manage. He became something of a feeding problem and I kept after him, though I knew I shouldn't. He never seemed to want to do what I wanted him to do. I reasoned, argued and I often got mad and yelled at him. Sometimes I spanked him, but it didn't work. When I've been angry with him I always feel guilty afterward. Each morning I resolve to be more patient, but then he seems to take advantage of me and pretty soon I'm cross again.

"The second and third are so easy by comparison. Whatever I do for them or to them seems to work right. And yet knowing how to manage them hasn't helped me with him."

Of course this is just a composite recital of what a certain number of parents say. Other families may have the same kind of tension, but much less in degree. Many others still don't fit into this picture at all. Of course, too, this same sort of tension may exist not between a parent and a first child, but between the parent and a second or later child. I believe only that it is more common with the first and sheds light on the kinds of pressures that often are felt by new parents.

Inexperience itself has an obvious effect, especially on those conscientious parents who lack all-round self-confidence. They doubt their capacities in this new business and so, like people nervously riding horseback for the first time, are alternately too timid and too assertive. (Children, like horses, quickly sense the insecurity.) I think, myself, that new parents with a lot of

education more often have doubts than those with less education, because in college it's clear that you either know your
lessons or you don't, and if you don't, you'll get caught. After
all, very few have had any lessons in baby care ahead of time.
(Thirty years out of medical school, I still have bad dreams about
taking an examination for which I haven't studied at all.)

☙ ☙ ☙

Probably most important of all for new parents are some of
the feelings — good and bad — left over from their own childhoods. The easiest way to become a successful parent is simply
to have had an enjoyable childhood with parents who were
loving, fair, consistent, and firm without much irritability. But
most people can't have parents who are quite that serene.

For most of us, the angriness or guiltiness that we felt at
moments toward our parents, the fears of not measuring up at
home, at school, the jealousy of brothers and sisters, have left
residues. These may get stirred up again when we become
parents, especially with our first child, or with a later child who
seems particularly significant to us.

Do such parental tensions have a bad effect? They are certainly
uncomfortable for the parents and for the child during the early
years. But if the tension is not excessive at the start and if it
shows signs of easing gradually as the years go by, the result by
late adolescence and early adulthood can be good in most
respects, and extra good in some respects.

I have been surprised and delighted to have several mothers
report to me in recent years that the first children about whom
they stewed and worried and reproached themselves fifteen or
twenty years ago, when we discussed them earnestly in my
office, have turned out not only happy but unusually successful
in such fields as medicine, teaching, social work, parenthood,
which involve sympathetic understanding of other people.

What can the explanation be? I suspect that the child who

has been sensitive and who had his troubles learning to get along with parents, brothers and sisters, and friends may, if he makes the grade, develop a greater interest in people and a stronger wish to work for them than the individual who has never had to give his relationships a thought. I'm not trying to say that it's better to have some unhappiness in childhood, but that there can be rich compensations for ordinary degrees of suffering.

Perhaps it should be added here that I don't want to leave the impression that *any* amount of maladjustment in a first child can be expected to be outgrown or to lead to good results in the end. A child in any position in the family who starts out somewhat unhappy can achieve happiness only with effort and with help. He is entitled to all the assistance that parents, teachers, school counselors, child psychiatrists, or family social workers can give.

Another encouraging aspect of being first-born is that though the parental devotion and concern may be uncomfortably intense, it can and often does, at the same time, give the child a basic sense of having a particularly important place in his family. As he grows up this is apt to be transformed into a feeling of having an important job to do in the world. He may also, in childhood, help himself over his rivalry with later children by coming to consider himself as a third parent to them, instead of a competitor. These feelings — of being particularly important *to* the parents and important *like* the parents — probably account in part for the optimism, drive, and sense of responsibility that are characteristic of so many first children.

It is interesting in this connection that a study of 1000 Americans who achieved positions of "eminence" showed that first-borns had this kind of success twice as often as those in other positions in the family. It's not that I or you think this is necessarily the best criterion of a successful life. But it should be reassuring, to parents who believe that they fuss too much with their first, to realize that it can have useful results for the world.

⟨ AVOIDING OVERDEPENDENCE

Many parents by the time they have several children comment on how much more independent the others are, compared with the first. They say, for instance, that the first has always had more trouble getting acquainted with outsiders and learning to enjoy rough-and-tumble play or that he is timid in the face of new situations or that he has always clung to the parents and demanded a lot of attention from them or that he is spoiled. Of course this comparison is not true of all families, or of even a majority. Sometimes it's the second or third child who is the most dependent, or there may be no such tendency in any of them. But it's safe to say that if overdependence shows up in any child in a family, it is more apt to be in the first.

When overdependency is developing in a child, the process is usually so gradual that the parents don't see it at the time. If he is the first in the family, they may become aware of it only after they have a second child, who is so independent by comparison.

There are two principal kinds of feelings in us parents which commonly make us hover over a first child and thus tie him more closely to us. The first is anxiety. Most of us are so inexperienced when we start with our first baby that we are anxious about everything: his hiccups, his temperature, his weight, his breathing. His first fall frightens us and overwhelms us with guilt. When he has his first nose cold, it seems like a major illness. Our overconcern shows in our faces, our voices, the speed with which we respond to his cry. Some of this anxiety rubs off onto him. Our fears about his physical safety usually tone down as the months go by. The same can't be said of our anxieties about his behavior and about our ability to control it. These worries become worse during the second year, when a baby ceases to be just a cute and compliant doll. He starts to show a whole collection of characteristics that we have been taught to view with concern — willfulness, obstinacy, defiance, temper, hostility, timidity. The interesting thing is that when a mother and child get into frequent wrangles with each other — about eating, toileting, doing all the other things he's meant to do, or not doing all the things he's not meant to do — it ties them more tightly to each other, despite their antagonism.

How do a majority of us parents manage to take minor misbehavior so much more casually in our later children? I suppose that part of the answer is that we have eventually learned with our first that we *can* control him somehow, by hook or by crook. With this assurance, we approach the second more calmly and therefore more effectively. At the very least we don't go looking for trouble — in the disciplinary sense. We assume everything is under control until proved wrong. So a lot of the possible issues never arise. As a result, the child is in a less touchy mood when we do have to interfere.

Just as important as our anxious feelings in tying a child to us are the feelings of delight we're apt to experience so very strongly in bringing up our first. When he smiles his first real smile, we are greedy for more. It's hard not to tickle him too much when we've heard his first belly laugh. We intimately share with him his discovery of his toes, his accomplishment in pat-a-cake, his pride in walking, his amazement at hearing his father's voice coming out of the telephone, his fascination with the first dog or cat he meets. As he becomes a little older, we can't wait to show him the zoo, the circus, a steam shovel in operation. The father is apt to buy electric trains about two years too soon and to get into enthusiastic demonstrations that would be more appropriate five years later.

All parents get down to the level of each of their children, occasionally, to play with them and to show them the wonders of the world. They wouldn't be ideal parents if they couldn't. This is good for parents and good for children.

But the problem of most of us, as we approach parenthood for the first time, is that we have such an accumulation of pent-up feelings — anxious uncertainty and joyful anticipation — that they come tumbling out in a flood to greet the first. Another way to say it is that to a certain extent we feel as though we are about to lead our lives all over again through our first child, with all the worries we developed while we were growing up (about our inadequacies and our naughtiness), and with all the hopes and ambitions we did realize and didn't realize in ourselves. Our first child is ourselves. We can't take him casually any more than we can take ourselves casually. No wonder it's something of a strain. (At its worst it's something like repeating an examination for a driver's license after you failed part of it the first time.)

☙ ☙ ☙

So far, this has been all theoretical discussion and not much practical help. I don't think there is any magical way to bring up a first child with the relaxation you will probably achieve with a second or third. Worry seems to go along with learning anything new. We've never found a way to teach medical students without their becoming anxious at one stage or another, and it must be the same with students of law, divinity, aviation, watchmaking, schoolteaching, and all the rest. Probably the most comfortable way to learn anything is in small doses from childhood on. This may be the main reason why farmers' sons follow in their fathers' footsteps more often than the sons of any other occupational group. To grow up in a pleasant family with a number of younger children is much the best way to learn child care, but it can't always be arranged.

However, I *do* think there are a number of practical steps that new parents can keep in mind that will lessen the chances of the

baby's becoming too dependent. Fortunately, in the first three
months of life babies are least aware of whether their parents
are nervous or not. They're too preoccupied with their inner
feelings — of hunger or sleepiness or colic.

From about three months on, they seem much more interested
in the outside world. Colic is usually about over, thank goodness, and it shouldn't be necessary for the parents to be carrying
the baby all evening. If he has developed the habit of expecting
this, it can always be broken by letting him cry briefly for a
couple of nights. It rarely takes longer than twenty minutes the
first night and five minutes the second. This is painful for the
parents to carry out, but when they see how well it works, they
are convinced it is right. This successful experience in separation
teaches the baby that he doesn't need to be so dependent on his
mother and father and it emancipates them from their own
overprotectiveness.

My own preference is that a baby should be on a fairly regular
feeding schedule, at least by three months of age, and in practically all cases a mother can gently educate her baby's digestion
to this by waking him up if necessary when the hour arrives and
steadily stretching the interval to four hours if he was a frequent
feeder to start with. I don't mean at all that an irregular, frequent schedule will always lead to dependence. What matters
is the mother's state of mind. I do think that an insecure mother
who hurries to the baby each time he stirs not only keeps him
trained to frequency and irregularity, but she teaches him that
he needs her quickly whenever he's the least bit uncomfortable.
She keeps her protectiveness at a high pitch for many months.
This helps to explain why some babies are still waking for a
couple of night feedings in the latter part of the first year, which
is certainly not necessary from a nutritional point of view.
When a baby and mother are accustomed to a regular schedule
by two or three months, each has developed a trust in the other's
dependability and a certain independence in himself.

I think that a very crucial period for fostering either independence or dependence is the last half of the first year. Now a baby is

able to sit up and, a little later, to creep, and to stand. His natural interest runs to handling objects all his waking hours: rattles, strings of beads, kitchen utensils, woolly toys, magazines. His wakeful periods have increased to several hours a day and he will keep himself busy and happy most of this time exploring around or, if he is in the playpen, putting toys out through the slats and retrieving them. He passes things from hand to hand, tastes them, chews on them. He has a moderate appreciation of company, especially his mother's, and tends to crawl back, from time to time, to the room she is in, as if to replenish his security. It's common for a mother of a first child to complain toward the end of the year that he cries each time she leaves the room, and this suggests how easily a small child picks up a bit of overconcern in a parent and matches it with a bit of overdependence.

A few parents get into quite a jam with the first baby in this six-to-twelve month period if they are too unsure of themselves to be able to resist his demands for attention — night or day — or can't resist the temptation to play with him most of his waking hours.

Some babies who previously have been sleeping soundly all through the night begin to be wakeful around the middle of the first year. This may start with a bad cold or ear infection which alarms the parents and makes them quick to run in to pick him up on subsequent nights if he whimpers or stirs. Sometimes it seems to be just teething that causes the waking. But if a baby learns that by crying he can always get picked up and given a bottle and a sociable time, and if he finds that by increasing his demands he can always bully his parents into prolonging the midnight party, he may eventually have his parents up for an hour and a half, two or three times each night. This is exhausting for everybody. The sequence here is that the baby's discomfort or illness stirs up the parents' anxiety. The parents' anxiety, expressed in hurrying in to pick him up, convinces him that he is really in desperate need of being rescued from his lonely bed. The parents' submissiveness feeds his demandingness. It doesn't take long for the parents to become resentful of the hard life he's giving them, but they don't know just what to blame him for. They feel ashamed of their angriness and submit further.

This nightly waking can be cured in a couple of nights if the parents can be convinced that it's no better for the baby than it is for them. They must stop going in to him, even once. After a few minutes of loud crying he realizes there's nothing to be gained and falls asleep. He will also be reassured by the nonappearance of his parents that they must believe there is nothing to be afraid of after all.

Daytime dependence on the part of a baby can creep up on a mother who is either too delighted to play with him constantly or too unsure of herself to refuse. The first type is apt to turn into the second in a few weeks or months. Soon after the baby wakes in midafternoon the mother gets involved in games like "This is the way the farmer rides" or peekaboo or pat-a-cake or dancing to music or just carrying him around in her arms. There's almost continuous conversation. After a few weeks of this, a baby is apt to lose most of his ability to amuse himself. When his mother, tired out, tries to set him down, he whimpers immediately and stretches out his arms. If she can never resist the appeal, it's as if she were saying to him, "You're right, it's lonely and perhaps dangerous to be anywhere else than in your mother's arms." I think, too, that the resentment accumulating inside her — at having to be a slave — probably gets through to him. It makes him uneasy, but it also challenges him to bully her again.

Naturally a mother wants to play with her baby at times, and to talk to him as she goes about her activities. But it generally works better to save most of the play together until the end of the wakeful period. And when she has played with him at other times, she needs to have enough assurance to get back to her work or her reading without apology. If he cries, she should remind herself that there is no realistic cause for her to feel anxious or guilty, and cheerfully tell him off.

When a baby has become intensely dependent, the process of mutual emancipation may be quite painful and drawn out — but it should be undertaken. The mother may need support from a psychiatrist or a family agency. She'll have to develop strong nerves to ignore the wails while she insists on going about her business. A practical point, when she does have time for play, is to sit down on the floor with the baby. Then if he ever becomes bored with standing in her lap, he can crawl away. But if she picks him up, there'll always be trouble when she sets him down again.

In the second year the child is even more at a fork in the road between independence and dependence. He can walk now and he has the urge to explore in ever-widening circles. He is much more interested in other people and children as separate personalities. He will want to approach them and make friends, in a simple fashion. (He holds things out to them and then takes them back, or he piles countless objects in their laps.) On the other hand, he becomes even more aware of his dependence on his mother for his security and rushes to her when hurt or frightened. In regard to strangers, he must have time to size them up before he approaches them. If they crowd him too soon, it pushes him back to his mother's skirts.

It is certainly important for the development of his independence that he and his mother not become involved in feeding problems, toilet-training struggles, and disciplinary issues. In serious conflicts in these areas the child and mother get tied to each other with tight, complex bonds which are partly hostile, partly anxious, and partly guilty. They can't get along together, but they can't forget each other or leave each other alone.

At a more simple level there are two procedures that a mother can keep in mind, especially if she senses a tendency to overprotectiveness in herself. The first is to resist the impulse to jump to the child's rescue whenever he gets himself involved in mildly dangerous maneuvers like climbing up on chairs or crawling into cupboards. If left to himself, he can usually solve these problems. If the mother anxiously rushes to his rescue, it convinces him that there are dangers all about and that he needs a mother's constant attention to survive.

The other method is to take him daily, if possible, where other small children play. Then he can learn how many kinds there are in the human race, that children are noisy and rough and often mean compared with adults, but that despite this they are the most fun of all to be with. Here again the protective mother may find herself watching him constantly and springing to his protection if he appears to be menaced by another child. Of course she should interfere if the danger is real or if he is being increasingly intimidated by a bully. She may even have to pick another playground. But first she should give him a reasonable opportunity to learn how to defend himself in minor squabbles. This is what she will see other mothers doing and it will come more naturally to her when she has her second.

I think that a majority of us will continue to tend to make our first-born somewhat dependent, because that's the way we're made, but that by being aware of the more common pitfalls we can hold this to a reasonable minimum.

THE NEW BABY AND
THE DISPLACED CHILD

Jealousy can be a
constructive experience.

I THINK a small child's jealousy of a baby used to be considered a sin by a majority of mothers, and there are still some who feel this way. When I would ask how the two-year-old was accepting the new arrival, I was amazed how often the mother would say, in a protesting tone, "Oh, doctor, he *loves* her. He constantly wants to pat her and hug her. Sometimes he doesn't realize how hard he's doing it and he makes her cry." It made me feel like an evil-minded man to keep thinking that such behavior was partly jealousy, when so many mothers were insisting on calling it 110 per cent love. When I asked my own mother some years ago about how I and my own brothers and sisters each in turn took to the birth of the next baby, she sprang to our defense. "Thank goodness none of my children showed any jealousy," she said. That's hard for me to believe now.

When I said "sin" I wasn't really joking. I meant that most parents felt that jealousy of a baby was so wrong that they couldn't admit it — even to themselves — they *had* to call it enthusiastic affection or thoughtlessness.

Of course the doctors and educators who have been pointing out the frequency of jealousy have not been doing it in order to give children a bad name. We have known how severely some children are hurt by jealousy and we have wanted parents to realize how natural and common it is so that they can help their children over it.

One of the hardest jobs in earlier days, when so many parents were trying to deny jealousy, was to get them to sense how devastating it can feel to a very small first child. He can't bury himself in a book or go to a far-off place to forget it all. He doesn't have a job to which he can turn for distraction. He doesn't have a choice of good friends from whom he can get consolation. His whole life is in his home and his whole security comes from the parents who, he feels, have turned away from him.

The best job of dramatizing his plight that I ever heard was done by a woman psychiatrist giving a talk at the Child Study Association in New York. She said to the mothers assembled, "Imagine what it would feel like if your husband came home from work one afternoon, leading by the hand a gorgeous hussy, and said to you, 'I've decided that since it has been good to have one wife, it will be even better to have two. I love this girl Marilyn and I know you'll love her too.'" It's preposterous to think that a wife could be delighted with such a stranger just because her husband expected it, but that's just what we expect of the very young child.

From my experience I think that most young children show some mixture of love and resentment for the baby who displaces them from the youngest position in the family. Even when no resentment shows on the surface, it seems to me fairer to assume that the child has at least occasional twinges of it, underneath. The proportions of delight and dislike will vary tremendously, depending on the child's nature and his situation in the family. On the average the first child, having assumed all his life that he has his parents to himself, will show the greatest strain, but this is certainly not true in many individual cases. The child who has had lots of experiences with other children and the one who is relatively independent of his mother are apt to be less upset. By the age of four or five a child is much less likely to show gross disturbances of behavior, because he feels so much more grown up than the baby and less dependent on his parents' attention.

Of course even in earlier days parents would have to face the fact of jealousy when it took uninhibited form: the direct attack with a heavy object, the deliberate push, the mean pinch. I think that parents have usually been able to accept jealousy that was expressed in polite verbal form. The classical example is the child's statement, after the baby has been home a couple of days, "You can take him back to the hospital now." Perhaps parents have felt that as long as a child wasn't aware himself of just how sharp his feelings were, they could accept his jealousy with a smile.

Many young children react to the feeling of being displaced not so much by antagonism as by what the psychiatrist calls regression. This means slipping back to a more babyish stage of development, in an effort to find comfort and security there. Common examples are wanting a bottle again, wetting at night or in the daytime or even soiling, reverting to baby talk, wanting to be fed by the mother again. In one sense regression is a less desirable way for a child to respond than if he becomes angry, knows just whom he's mad at, and tries to get even. In the latter case he's refusing to surrender and is going into action to defend his rights. In regression he's been knocked a little groggy and is in retreat. Actually the ordinary symptoms of regression are so common and are usually so temporary that we realize they are not serious under these circumstances. But when they are severe and persistent, when the child is acting like a woebegone baby all day long, it's time to come to his rescue with psychiatric help if necessary.

After more than twenty years during which doctors, nurses, and other parent educators have called so much attention to jealousy, most parents have come to assume it is normal and have worked conscientiously to help their children make the best of it, knowing that this is all that can be expected. Nowadays it's only a small proportion of parents who try to deny it. But another small number get into unnecessary trouble, I think, by developing an excessive fear of it. This may induce them to pay an exaggerated amount of attention to the displaced child, allow him unreasonable privileges, let him get away with demanding or even rude behavior. When he catches them enjoying the baby, they may startle as guiltily as criminals caught in the act. No child can remain secure or happy when he senses submissiveness in his parents. When they act as though they'd done him wrong, it convinces him that they must have. This increases the jealousy. I think that the excessive fear of jealousy is based on two false assumptions: that it's usually severe and that it's all to the bad. Probably the heavy emphasis that I and other writers have put on it — insisting that it's universal and that it ought to be coped with — is to blame for the dread that has been generated in some parents, particularly the very sensitive, conscientious ones, and those who suffered greatly from jealousy in their own childhoods.

☙ ☙ ☙

In any case, I want to point out some of the constructive influences that the birth of a baby can have — and usually does have — on a child. It can foster, it can speed up, it can strengthen his maturing. A very simple and clear example, which I admit doesn't happen very often, is the child of about two who surprises his mother by abruptly accepting toilet training or becoming dry at night or giving up his bottle when the baby arrives. The great contrast between the baby and himself — in size, in abilities, in behavior — apparently makes him suddenly realize how grown up he is, gives him pride in this, and stimulates him to go further still. Such cases, though rare, should

remind us that even the child who reacts in the usual babyish
way, by reverting to the bottle or wetting, must also have become acutely aware of how far away he is from infancy; there is
always the possibility of using this awareness positively by appealing to his grown-up side. To put it another way, the only
child probably feels most of the time that he is stalled; he hears
that he will be grown up some day, but he can't feel much
change from day to day or month to month. The arrival of the
baby gives a vivid new perspective on his own life. He suddenly
realizes that there is a speedway stretching from infancy to
adulthood and that he has traveled a surprising distance along
it. To be sure, his temporary security makes him have strong
impulses to dash back along this speedway. But he must, at the
same time, be more conscious of the forward direction of the
same road.

 I think the parent can help him to feel the pride and the
challenge by calling attention at times, in a gently pitying tone,
to the baby's inability to sit, walk, run, talk, understand, use a
spoon, cup or toilet, go out, play with toys, and so on. All the
baby can do is suck warm milk and cry. The parent at other moments can be on the lookout for opportunities to compliment
the child on new achievements and skills, to ask for his help
occasionally in a polite, grown-up manner, and then show appreciation in the same spirit, to grant him new privileges, however slight, as a consequence of increased ability or reliability,
to remind him of other skills and privileges which are just
around the corner. This two-sided campaign, if carried out
tactfully and truthfully, is quite legitimate. Its purpose is to
help him keep a sense of balance and to get full enjoyment of
his grown-upness, at a time when stresses are apt to make him
forget both.

Sometimes he will make a direct comparison between himself
and the baby and ask his parents to agree that he is smarter or
stronger. I think it is all right for the parent to agree occasionally, and the mother might add that she would be in a terrible
jam if she didn't have so much help from him. But I do believe

that the parent should not go in for direct comparisons between her two children from *her* point of view, as if she were appreciating one more than the other or loving one more than the other. Parental expressions of comparison or preference sharpen rivalry. They give the child the sense that the parent is a player of favorites. Even if he seems always to be judged the favorite, it can't help but remind him of the possibility of falling from favor, the necessity of frequently reassuring himself that he still has it. The campaign I've been advocating consists in reminding the child of the inherent disadvantages of babyhood from *his* point of view, the delights from *his* point of view in being older.

One other caution about this program should be mentioned. If a child who has been hard hit by jealousy seems more inclined to regress to babyhood than to feel any pride in being big and *if* the parents are too insistent in calling everything babyish that the child wants to experience and everything grown up that he doesn't want to do, he only becomes more totally convinced that a baby is just exactly what he wants to be. In other words, there must be some signs that the child responds to the appeal of grown-upness if it's to help.

🕊 🕊 🕊

Another aspect of helping the young child to move ahead when a baby comes has to do with encouraging him to feel — to some degree — like a parent. To be sure, this is another form of being grown up, but it's very special. It isn't just taking pride in greater size and capability, which apply to every succeeding stage of childhood. It implies a great leap ahead all the way to adulthood. Boys and girls, especially in the three-to-six-year-old stage, are normally fascinated with acting like fathers and mothers, even if no baby comes along. I think it is the strongest drive at this age and will operate without any encouragement from the parents. But when the arrival of a baby tends temporarily to produce regression and to discourage progression, the mother can tip the scales back again by stimulating the urge to play parent. The child escapes to some degree from the painful situation of being a rivalrous child by pretending that he is completely out of childhood. He convinces himself that he is not in the same league with the baby at all, but approaches him from an entirely new angle as a sort of third parent. His jealous feelings are actually transmuted into grown-up altruistic ones.

The techniques are well known to many parents: calling the baby "our baby"; encouraging the child to play a responsible role in fetching his bottle from the refrigerator or a diaper from the pile; helping the mother to dry him after the bath; asking the child to watch the baby while the mother is busy or out of the room; having the child take a visitor into the baby's room to show him off. A tactful mother can think of a dozen ways each day in which the child can feel that he and she are working side by side with a common purpose, even if the jobs are actually more of a hindrance than a help. After a while the help may actually prove helpful. In a less direct way a little girl may find equal satisfaction in caring for her doll in a way that exactly mimics her mother, in technique and in spirit.

There are several obvious limits to this approach. The mother dares not permit the child to perform certain jobs, such as carrying the baby around. On the other hand, the craving to hold the baby is so strong in young children that I think it's worth the trouble and the slight risk to arrange the child and baby on a sofa or on the floor so if the baby is dropped it won't be far.

Another limitation is that the impulse to play parent and to feel like a parent is distinctly less under the age of three. One can't say that there is always a small amount at two and a half and a fair amount at two and three quarters. It varies greatly in different children, depending on the sex of the child, his temperament, his ease in getting along with his mother.

Certainly a most important limitation is the degree to which the child enjoys playing parent. There is no point in the mother's imposing the role on a reluctant child. If he has no enjoyment of parenthood, the jobs will only increase his dislike of the baby, or at least his feeling that the baby is a prime nuisance. And neither boy nor girl should be encouraged to be parent all day long. He should still have plenty of chances to be a romping irresponsible child and to be playing with his friends.

I also think that the parent should not put the emphasis on the fun of baby care. Frequently the jealous child will prefer to play the part of a rather controlling and disapproving parent. The child who escapes from jealousy only to become a cross, bossy parent hasn't made much progress and will be a pain in the neck to friends and younger brothers and sisters.

᭐ ᭐ ᭐

There's a third way in which jealousy can be a constructive experience. If a child does not become too seriously upset by it, and is helped by tactful, loving parents to outgrow it gradually, I think he can end up with a stronger character. For a while he imagined that the baby was going to come between his parents and himself. He feared that they would never love him as much as they had before and he perhaps felt more resentment than love for the baby. But he becomes convinced as the weeks and months go by that his parents are just as devoted to him as ever. Reassured by this, he is better able to enjoy the good points in the baby and he develops an increasing fondness for him. It isn't just that he's got back almost to the state he was in before the baby was ever heard of. Since he has lived through a real crisis and has not been defeated by it, he must have been strengthened. He must end up surer of parents' love, more tolerant of other children, more serene about life and his ability to cope with it. The same kind of thing happens after a soldier goes successfully through his first battle, a mother through her first childbirth, a child through an operation. "The blade is tempered by the fire." I assume that this is why the first child in a family is so often able to show mostly affection and very little jealousy of the third.

☙ ☙ ☙

Many parents have written to me pointing out that the advice so often given — to prepare the child for the birth of a baby — has only limited application under the age of three and almost none under the age of two. I agree. No matter how patiently you try to explain the coming event to a one-year-old, you have the feeling that not much is getting through. He may be able to repeat words. He may be able to form a dim picture as the crib and the layette are made ready. It may interest him to read a picture book about the new baby.* But he certainly is not prepared for the feelings he will have when he sees his mother actually caring for the infant. So I don't think the parent should work at it too hard. It is worth while to make any shifts in living arrangements months ahead of time so that he doesn't feel dispossessed when the rival appears. But for the most part the parents must count on their tact and considerateness after the infant arrives. The core of the matter is to avoid the excessive enthusiasm for the baby, the preoccupation with him. This is hard to carry out because there is something about a baby that seems to call forth the doting attitude of parents, grandparents, and friends. But it is unnecessary to ignore the baby altogether. Even a one-year-old has some capacity for affection for him and is helped to increase it by identifying with the affectionate parent. And there is no point in the parents trying to heap large doses of

---

* *A Tiny Baby for You* by Nancy Langstaff and Suzanne Szasz. Harcourt, Brace & Co., Inc., New York. $2.50.

Our Baby by Miss Frances. (Ding Dong School Book No. 8.) Golden Press, Inc., New York. $ .25

The New Baby by Ruth and Harold Shane. (Little Golden Book No. 291.) Golden Press, Inc., New York. $ .25

forced attention on the child. What will reassure him most is realizing throughout the day that his mother and father are not forgetting him, but are talking with him, helping him, occasionally playing with him, keeping tuned to him, in the relaxed, assured manner they always had.

There is no doubt that one of the parents' jobs is to keep the one- or two- or three-year-old from actually hurting the baby, whenever possible, by such methods as watchfulness, very firm prohibition, prompt interference, keeping the baby, if necessary, in a closed room when he is asleep and the mother is busy. Though a small child may not be able to resist the urge to be mean, he feels very guilty if he succeeds. He, as well as the baby, needs protection from his hostile feelings.

And finally, everything we have learned from child-guidance work reinforces our conviction that it helps the child to be able to *talk* about his jealous feelings. (This is very different from letting him carry them into action.) When he has tried to be mean and has been stopped, or when his mother detects that he's feeling angry or depressed, she can remind him again that she knows he feels cross at the baby sometimes, knows he would sometimes like the baby to go away so that he could be alone with mommy and daddy. This usually brings temporary improvement in spirits and a permanent improvement with time. It keeps him from feeling unbearably guilty. It makes it unnecessary for him to hide his antagonism deep inside where it would last longer and do more harm to his character. It shows the child in the most convincing way that his mother is still thinking of him and loving him, which in the long run is what will get him over his despair.

CHILDREN'S
QUARRELS

*The parent's cue is to deal with
each child as an individual.*

ᐊᐧ

EVERY WEEK brings at least one letter about squabbling and fighting between children in the family. These mothers who have enough of a problem to make them write letters sound frustrated and exhausted. I've visited families occasionally where the fighting was so continuous that I felt tired and edgy at the end of twenty minutes. I always assumed that when things got that scrappy (shouts, screams for mother, thuds, crashes, wails, complaints to mother, countercomplaints — all day long) the pattern was fixed for good. But I well remember the amazement of a mother and myself, once, at how fast the picture can change. She and the father decided, rather guiltily, to take a two-week vacation without their three battling and somewhat undisciplined children (four to eight years of age). They happened to be able to engage a children's nurse with an excellent reputation to hold the fort. After a couple of days away they called home to see if the nurse and children were still alive and were told in a cheerful voice that everyone was fine. It was hard to believe, but a letter from the grandmother, who dropped in to see the children daily, confirmed the story. Everyone was having such a good time that the parents stretched their vacation an extra week. And when they came home they were astonished all over again. The children were cheerful and friendly with one another, co-operative and polite with the nurse. The mother said that the sight of them curled up on the sofa together listening to the nurse read a story reminded her of the passage "The lion shall lie down with the lamb."

There are many factors that make for quarrelsomeness, and they vary in kind and intensity in different families. We might start with a couple of the more serious and unusual types. There is the child who is chronically aggressive. He bullies not only brothers and sisters but anyone in the neighborhood if he thinks he can get away with it. Usually there is a lot of tension between him and his parents, which goes way back into early childhood. This kind usually requires the aid of a guidance clinic or a family social agency to straighten out. Another chronic type is the child whose antagonism makes him look for trouble but who is so constituted that he manages to provoke other children to pick on him — he always ends up the victim. Such a child needs professional help even more than the bully because his unhappy pattern is less likely to improve by itself with age.

A very important factor is how consistent the parents are in wanting serenity in the home. You may think that all parents want it. Certainly all parents believe they do. Yet there are some who are only going through the motions of commanding their children to stop fighting. They have no conviction or authority in their voices. They have no follow-through. They get no results. What they think are orders are really only complaints. Such parents really expect their children to fight and unconsciously they seem to get a certain perverse satisfaction out of it. They almost boast of the turmoil to the neighbors, sometimes in the presence of the children themselves, or they grin and shrug their shoulders. This represents a subtle resignation to unpleasantness, usually carried over from a similarly turbulent childhood. Those parents who really don't like fight- ing can at least keep it below the uproar level, even though the children may continue to give each other dirty looks and mutter under their breaths. Of course all of us have our off days when we surrender some of our control over our children and let the storms rage. But parents who can never keep things in check need and can profit from professional help.

Somewhat separate from the matter of parental control is parental tension. I think almost all of us have been aware at one time or another that when we are closest to being on an even keel ourselves (things going well at the office, social life satisfying, no unusual worries about the children or health or finances), the amount of antagonism between the children decreases notice- ably. And anything that makes us irritable is apt to increase the children's fights. To put it simply: if a child (like any other human being) feels picked on and can't retaliate directly, he has an irresistible urge to pick on someone else of a size he can manage.

☙ ☙ ☙

Of all the factors that make for ordinary quarreling between children, I think that jealousy is by far the most potent. The strongest attachment in childhood is of course the one between the child and his parents. To some degree he wants the parents' love for himself alone, and fears that the affection which goes out to brothers and sisters will be subtracted from his share. This makes him suspicious and resentful of them. The degree varies enormously, depending on circumstances and what each child is used to. The first child, who was an only child for a couple of years and took it for granted that both parents be- longed exclusively to him, is, on the average, much more likely to be upset by the arrival of a baby than a subsequent child who has been used to sharing the parents from the start. Quite similar variations occur in business organizations when a new person joins the staff, or in the field of friendships.

We have to realize that this possessive, jealous element in love is not simply an unfortunate flaw in the character of man. It is part of the essence of our humanness. It's part of what makes us stick together as husband and wife, as families, and as other groups. Otherwise our relationships would be as casual as the relationships of insects.

Children who are close to each other in age tend to fight most. The younger is the one who has displaced the next older from the baby position in the family, and in many ways that's the hardest position to give up. As the older one persecutes the younger, it doesn't take the latter too long to find who his special enemy in the family is. Of course there are other reasons why those closest to each other fight most. They are thrown together in family arrangements. They are interested in the same playthings and the same companions.

Much depends on the personality and physique of each of the children. I think some babies are born more agreeable and some more assertive and I imagine the assertive ones will be more likely to raise a fuss if they feel left out. A slow child in a smart family, a homely girl set among beauties, a short boy among tall brothers, a girl born to parents who much prefer boys may be excessively jealous, if other conditions in the family favor rivalry.

Next we ought to consider what influence the parents' attitudes toward the children have on jealousy. Right away we're apt to jump to the conclusion that inequality in the love of a parent for two children is a powerful generator of rivalry. That's what so many fairy stories and novels and people seem to say. But I don't think it's that simple. It brings up a tricky question: Is there such a thing as equal love?

I think that good parents are equally devoted to each child but that they can't possibly enjoy or be irritated by any two in the same way; therefore they shouldn't try to treat them exactly the same (same number of minutes of attention, same number of smiles, same number of frowns). Children and adults are not fooled by an attitude that's forced. In the long run they don't really like to be compared with others — either favorably or unfavorably. What each wants most, I think, is to be loved and enjoyed for himself. If a child feels sure that he has a good niche in his parent's heart he doesn't worry so much about his brothers' and sisters' niches — *unless*, that is, the parent keeps comparing the niches or threatening to oust a child from his niche. This, I think, is the essence of the problem of handling jealousy or preventing it.

The easiest way for a parent to stir up jealousy is to keep comparing a child unfavorably with his brother. It's a double-edged sword that makes him feel definitely rejected by the parent and makes him resent his brother for being so openly favored. Most parents know this and are too tactful to try to use such a method for correcting a child.

However, I think that many conscientious parents use another form of comparison which they believe to be a preventive of jealousy but which really is a stimulator of it. They try whenever it's humanly possibly to give *exactly* the same presents and privileges to all their children, at least to those who are close together in age. Furthermore, they're apt to call attention to the equality of treatment. If one boy gets a blue toy car, the other gets a blue car. If one daughter is to have a new winter coat, the other receives one, too, even if she doesn't really need it. If one child goes shopping with mother or on a trip with father, the parents are careful to arrange and announce the same privilege for each of the others in due time. I remember a harassed mother whose four young children fought particularly fiercely about who was to sit next to her at table. She had to keep an elaborate chart which indicated in what order the children changed places around her, three meals a day, seven days a week.

The question we have to ask sharply is whether such legalistic forms of justice decrease rivalry. They certainly do not, in my opinion. The parents who have used them or been driven into them by the demands of their children are the first to admit that these children — all day long — are suspiciously watching one another and their parents to make sure that no advantage is given or taken, and keeping up a noisy wrangling.

These precautions against unfairness constantly remind the child that there must be a real danger of unfairness unless everybody watches out. The fact that the parents co-operate in the precautions means to the child that the parents are afraid that they themselves will be tempted to be unfair. I think that this is the crux of the matter: the parents who are maneuvered into these legalities really *don't* have enough confidence in their impartiality. They have probably carried over from their own childhoods too strong a sense of guilt about the jealousies they felt in relation to their brothers and sisters. They are afraid that if they inadvertently show any favoritism to one child they'll be resented by another, just the way they resent it when their parents seemed to show favoritism to a brother or sister. So they lean over backward.

I'd say to a parent who was trying too hard to be scrupulously fair: Don't feel you have to buy identical toys (unless there's a very practical reason); and if the boys complain, tell them you'll take both toys back if you hear another word out of them. If your daughter objects because you didn't get a new coat for her, too, just remind her that she doesn't need one yet. If there's argument at meals about seating, tell them that everybody in this family is going to continue to sit just where he has always sat. The fierceness of tone that I seem to have put into the parent's voice in these examples isn't really necessary. The only necessity is that the parent show that he isn't the least bit afraid he's discriminating and that he's not going to be bullied into acting as if he were. The cue is to deal with each child as an individual. Praise him or correct him or give him a present or buy him a coat or set his bedtime or give him duties or expect school grades on the basis of what's right for him. Keep the other children out of the conversation and out of your mind.

᙭ ᙭ ᙭

There's one more subdivision of this topic that to me has great practical importance: how do you manage the squabbles themselves? Conscientious parents often try to act as the judge: Who started it? Who did what to whom? Who is to be called the culprit? What's the proper punishment? I think myself that this judging is a trap, which wise parents had better dodge as much as possible. If I'm right that jealousy is one of the principal motives that make children pick fights with each other in the first place, then the readiness of a parent to enter the picture each time as a judge emphasizes and accentuates the jealousy factor. The child comes to realize that each quarrel is an opportunity to prove triumphantly that his parent approves of him and disapproves of his brother. So quarreling acquires more purpose and appeal for him. Of course he knows that he can't openly start a battle or he'd be judged the villain. But a jealous child always feels that the other one is really the aggressor, so all he has to do is watch him suspiciously for signs of it. (He can find or imagine a hundred excuses any day.) Then he joins battle as the injured party. To put it in other words, the parent's favor becomes a prize, an added inducement for every squabble, and thus a stimulator of more quarrels.

But don't parents have to stop fights? Some they do and some they don't. When two young children of about equal power occasionally tangle (their sizes and ages may be quite different), I think they will often learn more about how to get along with each other if left to argue it out or tug it out or whack it out. I'd at least give this method a few tries. But if one always pulverizes the other and makes him more timid, it's the wrong system.

The amount of squabbling will also be a determining factor in whether the parents are willing to allow it to occur. There will naturally be difference of opinion about this. Most parents would overlook a couple of minor spats a day and a bigger fight occasionally. But most wouldn't willingly permit their children to battle a good part of the day, for either their children's sake or their own.

If the parents do need to interfere — because one child is bullying another or because the quarrels are too frequent or too fierce or too noisy for comfort — I think they can usually do this just as efficiently without judging or taking sides, and that in the long run this will make for fewer fights rather than more. They can simply insist that the fighting stop. They can refuse to listen to the complaints. If they really mean it and see to it that the children break it up and if they immediately interfere again in case the battle resumes, the children will be convinced and will obey, just as they comply with any prohibition about which the parents are determined and consistent.

III

Discipline and Companionship

"HOW DO I MAKE HIM MIND?"

Parents have to be reasonably consistent and
act as if they expected to be obeyed.

"How do I make him mind?" is the most frequent question of some mothers. Actually it's not so much a question, because they don't really expect an answer from the relative or doctor or teacher they are speaking to. It's more a complaint — that the child is unmanageable — and an appeal for agreement and sympathy. Of course we all lose control of our children occasionally, but I want to talk about the few unhappy parents who hardly ever seem to have it, because we can see the issues more clearly in these exaggerated cases.

The answer to such a parent might be another question: "Do you really mean it, when you ask your child to obey?" The parent would naturally and sincerely say yes, but this would be only partly true. If you or I were watching her during a disciplinary crisis (let's say it's the mother, not because fathers don't have such difficulties but because it's easier to say "her" for the mother and to pretend that all the bad children are "he"), we'd probably be able to spot the trouble right away. (If she saw you or me having trouble with our child she'd be able to see how we got off on the wrong foot, too; it's always clearer in the case of somebody else.)

Here are some examples that I've seen firsthand:

A doesn't seem to notice when her small child is playing with his milk — comes to only when the whole glass is spilled.

B calls out "Don't fool with your milk" when she sees the child starting to do just that and then turns away, though there is no evidence that the child has obeyed. She notices again only when the milk goes over.

C gives her boy a slap when she catches him climbing up on the fender of the car, but when she sees him doing it again two minutes later she doesn't say or do anything.

D, when her son climbs up on the fender again, says — in his hearing — to a friend, "See, I can't do a thing with him."

E is heard shouting threats all day long ("I'll put you to bed; I'll call the cops; I'll give you a good licking"), but as far as the neighbors can see, the threats don't do any good and she never carries out any of them.

F starts to scold her son (for being mean to a neighbor). He turns on her, shouting, "I don't care, you dope." Surprisingly, she doesn't act shocked or punish him. She and he keep raising their voices a notch as they holler back and forth until one or the other gets bored and wanders away.

G, leaving her son at kindergarten for the first time, tells the teacher, in front of him, "He's a holy terror." (The teacher has no trouble with him.)

H's one-year-old wanders innocently into the living room and she says instantly, "Now don't touch the TV." He hadn't thought of it, but now, challenged, he inches toward it while his mother sits still, glaring at him. She turns to a visitor and says, "See what I mean?"

J, whose father was an alcoholic, asks suspiciously of her sixteen-year-old son who has been to a party, "Did you take a drink?" (He didn't.)

The next and last example is a little different, but belongs in our discussion. A first-born baby is brought to K, his mother, for the first time in the hospital, with his thumb in his mouth. She says "Naughty boy!" — not jokingly but crossly.

Maybe you've become irritated with such a succession of bad examples and think they are too exaggerated. They're exaggerated, but they're all quite real. They bring out several of the factors that get in the way of good discipline. Parents in situations like these *think* they are trying to make their children behave, and I am sure that consciously they want them to. But we can see that some of them at best are only half trying, others are not trying at all and some, without realizing it, are suggesting that their children misbehave.

It's also clear in some of the examples that to a certain extent the parents expect their children to be bad (even from birth!) and don't really expect to be able to control them. Such attitudes in parents are hard at first to believe and to understand. Child-guidance clinic work often shows, as you would expect, that the mother's situation in her own childhood was fairly similar. She was frequently called bad and expected to be bad and allowed to be bad (bad in the childish sense of naughty).

When she becomes a parent herself she takes on the methods of her parents and has all the appropriate feelings to go with them: mistrust of her child from the very beginning, no confidence in her own ability to know what's right and to teach it to her child, no sense of being entitled to respect from him, a readiness to squabble, even a subtle enjoyment of it.

Well, that's enough of the distressing examples. Parents who are thoroughly discouraged about their ability to manage their children need help from a family and children's social agency, a child-guidance clinic, or some other counselor to get an understanding of the roots of their difficulty.

🎜 🎜 🎜

The rest of us become discouraged only at moments. But each of us as a child was allowed at times to get away with misbehavior, was called bad, was left with confused feelings about certain parent-child situations. When we get into comparable spots with our own children, especially when we are at low ebb from other tensions, we slip out of our roles as leaders who know what we want them to do, and just wrangle with them at their level, as if we were all bad children together.

When we are in the right mood and on the right track, we find that we can manage our children without deep thought or great effort. Actually we are using a wide variety of elaborate and delicate methods, but with as little concern as a person who sits down at the piano and plays a piece he learned ten years before. The child does a lot of the work. We know we can depend most of the time on his wanting to please us because he loves us as we love him. As early as one year of age, and most intensively between three and six, he is trying to be grown up like us — in politeness, skillfulness, usefulness. In the school years he strives himself for conformity to the standards set by his friends and the school.

We generally manage our children in their earliest years by example, by positive suggestion, by distraction, by leading by the hand, by appealing to their desire to be grown up, by bodily removal. In the second year, when the child has some sense of what we want and don't want, we all begin gradually to rely more and more on verbal requests and prohibitions. We sense, with whatever leadership qualities we have, that we have to be reasonably consistent (perfection is fortunately not required), feel and speak and act as if we expected to be obeyed, and have at least a touch of friendliness in our tone of voice, such as we'd use in making a request of a friend. The last is the hardest to maintain through a long day. We've carried over enough disapproval from our upbringing so that we easily slip into the tone of irritation, the tone that says "I don't suppose you'll obey" or "I've been feeling cross with you and now I'm getting even with you by asking you to do something you don't like (or to stop doing something you enjoy)."

As our children learn what we expect of them, that we mean what we say, and that we say it for a good reason, they can be kept in line, most of the time, by brief directions and reminders.

We can express these constructive aspects of discipline in another way by saying simply that a mother senses that her main job is to lead her child positively. Ideally, when she sees things starting to go wrong she jumps in quickly and *prevents* misbehavior (she develops a sixth sense like radar, that operates all day, even when her children are hundreds of yards away). So she seldom has to call him bad because he doesn't get too many chances to be bad.

THE QUESTION OF
PUNISHMENT

Punishment is the substitute, emergency method
when the regular system of discipline breaks down.

EVERY TIME I have given a talk to a parent-teacher association,
and we have arrived at the question period, there has been a
solemn man in about the fifth row who slowly rises to his feet,
clears his throat and asks, in the deliberate tone of a district at-
torney, "Doctor, what is your opinion on punishment?" I always get the feeling that he has argued in favor of just punishment ever since the birth of his first child, that his wife has been
firmly opposed and has kept him from it on most occasions, and
that now he'd like to see if there aren't other people around
who'll take his side.

I don't mean by this example that fathers are generally pro-
punishment and that mothers are anti. Sometimes it's the other
way around. Most often the father and mother are on the same
side of the fence; but even when they approximately agree there
may be enough difference of opinion to cause arguments.

Certainly the newspapers consider punishment, especially physical punishment, an endlessly hot and fascinating topic. Whenever an educator or psychologist or physician in a long, careful speech about the management of children makes an incidental reference to the naturalness of occasional punishment, this side remark is what always gets into the headline as "Expert Advocates Corporal Punishment." It seems as if, to certain people, the most important question in all child care is whether to spank or not. There's something unhealthy in this obsession. Actually such overemphasis on the subject of punishment is nonsense. We all realize, if we stop to think about the upbringing of our schoolmates, friends, relatives, and selves, that some who were punished fairly often turned out well and some badly, and that those who were rarely if ever punished divided the same way.

☙ ☙ ☙

What is really important in the development of good discipline is the feeling of the parent toward the child and of the child toward the parent. And these are only two sides of the same coin. The methods of punishment — if any — are only incidental details.

We know that the most vital element of all is that the parents love the child in the sense of being devoted to him, wanting him to turn out well, enjoying his good qualities (not his bad ones). The warmth of their love is what fosters in him lovingness and lovableness. To be more specific, he's nice to people a majority of the time simply because he likes people (there's more agreeableness than disagreeableness in him). Furthermore, knowing how good it makes him feel to be loved and how uncomfortable, by contrast, to be disapproved of, he also behaves himself to keep people liking him. These two basic elements in discipline seem so obvious to most of us that we forget to consider them.

There's a third factor that's vital too. A child, particularly in the three-to-six-year-old period, expresses his devotion to his parents by molding himself in their image; not just in the sense of copying their skills, occupations, manner of speech, but genuinely trying to be civilized and responsible like them. This is how the boy acquires much of his desire to be co-operative with men, brave in danger, courteous to women, faithful to a job, just as his father is. This is how a girl is inspired to be helpful in the home, devoted to babies (live and doll babies), tender to other members of the family, as her mother is. In other words, children who are loved do a tremendous amount of work themselves developing their own characters and discipline.

But as every mother and father knows, this leaves plenty for the parent to do. However good a child's intentions are, he is still inexperienced, impulsive, easily led astray. Every hour of every day the parent must be saying, "When you give your sister a ride in your cart you should pull it slowly"; "You have to come to lunch now because it's ready"; "Remember, you mustn't change the phonograph records — that's mother's job"; "Don't cross the street unless a grownup is with you."

Furthermore, there are the other moments when the child doesn't *want* to behave, when he's resentful about something the parent or brother or sister or friend has done or failed to do. These stormy periods require firmness of an expert kind.

We have seen how there has to be a reasonable amount of consistency and sincerity in the guidance aspects of discipline. It's not that children can't adjust to variations in the rules — in different situations and with different adults. In fact, they are surprisingly adaptable. It's that the adult must really feel like a responsible person in charge, must expect the child to behave, and see that he does. The parent who has no confidence in himself as leader, no confidence in the child's preference to be good, tends to descend to a child's level — threatening, shouting, slapping without conviction, even subtly provoking the child to misbehavior.

Well, I started to talk about punishment, but I've had to take time to show that discipline largely depends on other factors.

Punishment is not the main thing that keeps a child from being bad, any more than punishment is the main thing that keeps you or me from robbery, arson, murder. Punishment is the substitute, emergency method when the regular system of discipline breaks down. Even then, punishment doesn't do much good unless there is a sound character underneath and a loving relationship, as all the cases of habitual criminals prove.

🚩 🚩 🚩

What causes the temporary breakdowns in discipline? Your child is tempted to play with a forbidden object that today looks more fascinating than ever (perhaps because he has grown up enough in the interval to see possibilities in it that he never saw before). He takes a chance that you weren't too serious when you prohibited it the last time and that he won't harm it anyway. Or through sheer carelessness he breaks something that's precious to you. Or he may be angry at you for seeming to be unfairly cross with him or to favor his brother. Perhaps he's slightly rude to you when you're tense about something else. Or he narrowly escapes being run over chasing a ball into the street. Indignation or righteous anger wells up in you. You punish, or at least you feel like punishing.

It is simply not possible to manage a child so smoothly that you don't get mad at him occasionally. This is nothing to feel guilty about. And when you are angry, I think it's of relatively minor importance whether you spank him or send him to his room or just glare at him.

I believe that whether a parent punishes or not, whether a parent spanks or not, depends most often on whether the parent was so punished in his own childhood.

Those parents brought up with very little punishment or none at all, because *their* parents had been able to maintain discipline by positive guidance and firmness alone, have usually absorbed the same attitudes of leadership and find punishment rarely necessary.

People who were themselves punished occasionally for good cause (probably the majority of Americans) come to it instinctively with their own children. If the relationship is generally sound, if the justification is clear, if the punishment is appropriate to the individual child, then the effect is usually wholesome. The child knows he had it coming to him and feels chastened rather than resentful. He is reminded in this emphatic way that the parent really did mean what he had said. The parent's anger and indignation are discharged. If the punishment was right, the air is cleared and the child will behave well in this respect for a reasonably long period.

Obviously I've left a lot of "ifs" in the last paragraph and I'll have to add some others. If a parent is having to punish a great deal, if the relationship between parent and child is a strained one, if the punishments leave the child resentful or intimidated (or if they leave the parent feeling chronically guilty), if they lead to no improvement in behavior, then they are not working right at all. Something is out of kilter in the parents' basic discipline or in the child's life and they both need the help of an understanding counselor — a psychiatrist or a worker in a family social agency, or a wise teacher or minister.

☙ ☙ ☙

When punishment is used, should it be immediate or delayed? Early in this century when it was widely believed that a parent could choose a theory of child rearing and then make it work by will power alone (ignoring the deeper feelings of parent *and* child), some people said that punishment should never be carried out in anger but only later, in an atmosphere of calm judgment. This was quite unrealistic and it missed the point that even the most reasonable of parents feels the urge at the moment when justifiably angry. However, this doesn't mean that there aren't occasions when a parent rightly wants to think it over and perhaps consult the other parent. In general, though, I think it's preferable for the punishment to be applied promptly and in a form that won't drag on. It's an agonizing business for a child to wait for hours to face his father and it's rough on the father who comes home hoping to relax to find that he must first be the grim disciplinarian. I myself feel that delayed judgment and delayed punishment should be avoided unless the situation is more serious than usual. And a punishment that is spread out over a week or two sometimes makes the whole family miserable.

If you are going to ask, "What forms of punishment are best?" I'm going to pass the buck back to you. There's no one answer any more than there's an answer to "Which is better, steak or ice cream?" or "Which color is prettier, red or blue?" The right punishment is the one which seems right to the parent and which works. It all depends on the parent, on the child, and on the misbehavior.

A slap on the hand or the behind works like a charm for one parent-child combination. Another mother only feels like a brute for hours afterward; and another child is made furiously resentful by this indignity. A brief isolation in his room sweetens up one child in five minutes. Another child makes the family wretched with his crying for the better part of an hour. Fines and withdrawal of privileges are more appropriate for the school-aged child, and when they are fair and not run into the ground they even appeal to his sense of justice. In another case, though, they lose all moral value and lead only to bookkeeping and arguing.

So there is no system of punishment that is neat or that will work the same in any two families or that will function automatically.

Punishment *alone* has never made a bad character into a good one, or even insured temporary good behavior.

Good discipline is mainly based on mutual love and respect. In childhood it has to be reinforced with teaching, firmness, re-

minders. Punishment is only one form of reminder, a particularly vigorous one for emergencies — usually with strong feelings
involved — to get a child back into the groove. If there is no
groove, the job is too great for punishment alone. The real work
of the parent is to keep the child out of trouble — by making it
ever clear to him what is expected and by stepping in early and
firmly when he starts to go wrong — rather than to let matters
get out of control and then have to decide whether to punish
and how. But it's often backbreaking work. And the harder
you've tried, the madder you get when the moments of failure
occur. It has been this way in every good family, I'm sure, since
the beginnings of the human race.

THE FATHER'S ROLE
IN DISCIPLINE

Children are more comfortable with fathers who
take an active role in discipline.

WHAT PART should a father take in discipline? By "discipline"
I don't mean merely punishment, but the much larger matter
of managing and leading a child successfully. I'll quote from
two mothers to show two opposite kinds of problems. "My
husband, a marvelous father, wants immediate compliance with
all commands, saying it might save our son's life if he were in a
dangerous position. I am more inclined to be lenient, feeling
that a small child (ours is fourteen months) isn't yet able to respond immediately." The other says: "Our little boy is two
years old. The problem is hitting — especially his father. My
husband says it is no fun to play with him because he continu-
ally slaps or pokes his eyes or hits him in the head with any toy
available. This isn't done in anger but with chortles of great
glee."

You might say right away that these aren't exclusively the
problems of fathers — some mothers have the same kind. That's

true, but I still think that these particular types come up more often with fathers.

Before we concentrate on fathers we ought to think about the different parts that mothers *and* fathers play in discipline. All you have to do is look around to see that it's somewhat different in every family, depending on the upbringing and personality of each parent and the nature of each child, which is as it should be.

A surprising number of mothers have told me that their husbands have better control over the children than they do. It makes them mad to have their husbands breeze in at the end of the day and manage the children more easily. Probably the main explanation is not that fathers have some kind of magic, but that a mother's discipline is more likely to wear thin because she's having to use it hour after hour all day.

Perhaps another reason is that men from early childhood have been taught to control their aggressiveness by means of constant drilling in the rules of conduct: "Play fair," "Be a good loser," "Don't hit a man when he's down," "Don't hit first, but it's all right to hit back." I suspect that this long training makes men able to lay down the rules to others with more conviction and authority. Most girls have less fierceness to start with and so they can be managed with less sternness. They grow up expecting to get along with others by means of personal persuasion rather than abstract rules. In fact they are apt to think that a lot of men's rules and laws are silly.

I think we should also remember that in most families the discipline works more easily — and at the same time more leniently — between opposite sexes. In a majority of families fathers aren't quite so strict with their daughters as they are with their sons, and yet their daughters may obey them more readily. And mothers are apt to give the benefit of the doubt to their sons. As parents we may not admit that we treat them any differently, but our children in talking with each other can often spot our attitudes. There's nothing mysterious or morbid about this. Human beings, like many other creatures, are made to be charming to the opposite sex and to be somewhat rivalrous with their own sex. This tends to be true even though fathers and sons love each other dearly, and mothers and daughters do the same. I hardly recognize my own father when I hear my sisters describe him. They emphasize that he was delightful, humorous, easygoing. I remember him as devoted, absolutely just, but very serious and quite strict. It isn't simply that the good father is apt to be more exacting with his sons, but that the sons *see* the father as even more awe-inspiring than he really is because of the rivalry that *they* feel toward him.

Another way of explaining why fathers are usually more strict with their sons is that fathers from the time that they were boys have been trying to live up to manly standards, been criticized by *their* fathers, and criticized themselves when they failed. And what we were criticized for when we were children we tend strongly to criticize in our children and others when we get older. Mothers, having spent many years being girls, are experts in what they expect of their daughters, too.

☙ ☙ ☙

Now it's time to get back to the particular problems that some fathers have. Take first the father who expects instant obedience of his fourteen-month-old son. If you'll let me do some guessing, I'll guess that this boy is the first child in the family. (With our second or third we're usually more relaxed.) I'll guess, too, that this father was more strictly brought up than average, with a special emphasis on the importance of prompt obedience. This didn't merely set a pattern or habit in him. It went much deeper into his feelings. When all of us were children and our parents scolded us sternly for certain acts that they said were dangerous or bad, we developed real anxiety about these consequences, even though we may have seemed to be paying little attention at the time. This is why, as young parents, we find ourselves jumping on our children so hard, before we've had a chance to think. The father in question must be truly afraid that his son will get into trouble if he doesn't acquire instantaneous obedience at fourteen months — however irrational that may sound to you and me — because of deep concerns carried over from his upbringing. The fact that his wife doesn't see this danger only increases his anxiety. Most of us are able to look at the one-year-old with more serenity and see that he is only ready for the first easy lessons in discipline and that there are many ways to keep him out of danger and misbehavior in addition to obedience.

Strictness may become accentuated, too, when a husband feels, for any one of a variety of reasons, that his wife is favoring the son, or is lining up with the son against him. This comes out dramatically in stories about the mean stepfather who resents the stepson who has been close to the mother much longer than he. But a father can come to feel this way about his own son, if he himself has always been an insecure person (perhaps since childhood when he felt that his mother preferred his younger brother); or if his wife is in actuality antagonistic toward him and is unconsciously using her closeness with her son to provoke quarrels.

Some of the factors in overseverity used to show up particularly clearly when a father came home from World War II, during which he had had to submit to the arbitrariness of military discipline. He would find a son two or three years old who had had all the comforts of home, who seemed to absorb 98 per cent of the wife's time and attention, and who didn't appear to have the dimmest idea of any kind of discipline. To add insult to injury, the boy was likely on his part to resent violently this giant who barged into his home and tried to act as if he owned the boy's beloved mother.

If the wife of a strict father tries to make up to the son for the father's sternness, it makes the father even more fearful that the boy is being spoiled, and therefore inclined to be more severe with him. Also, in the long run, the mother's efforts to protect the son make the father more antagonistic to both of them. This gives the boy a feeling that he and his mother are enemies of the father, which is unwholesome all around.

If the mother can curb her impulse to spring to the boy's defense, and keep out of sight when the father is being the disciplinarian, this will usually create the best situation for father and son to work out their relationship. If the mother can show her sympathetic understanding of her husband's anxiety about the boy's character, it may help to reduce the unrealistic element in the father's concern. If things have gone beyond these steps, it is worth making an effort to talk the problem over with some adviser in whom the father has confidence, such as a minister or doctor.

Now for the second example: the father who got buffeted about by the chortling two-year-old. He sounds exactly opposite from the severe father, but he isn't quite opposite. If you question such fathers you often get the answer, "I was treated too severely in my own childhood. I don't want my son ever to resent me the way I often resented my father." So both attitudes may come from being brought up sternly. But in one case the new father lines up with the grandfather in fearing what *lack of* discipline will do. In the other case the new father is afraid of what *too much* discipline will do. This may make the latter father so afraid to assert himself, or even to stand up for himself, that his child is almost invited to walk over him.

Every baby as he gets somewhere near the age of a year begins to toy with meanness, at moments when he's feeling cranky. He'll deliberately pull his mother's hair or sink his teeth into his father's cheek. The parent who's not afraid to be firm, knowing that a child needs constant guiding, promptly restrains the baby and shows in his facial expression a mild disapproval. If the baby tries again the parent automatically restrains him again. This mild lesson — that the parent doesn't like to be hurt, doesn't intend to let himself be hurt, will prevent the child from hurting him — sinks gently enough into the mind of even a one-year-old. He may not have learned the lesson for good the first time, but a few repetitions will do the job reasonably well.

But if the parent is so afraid of showing firmness (it's really the fear of showing anger) that he lets the baby get away with the attack, then the child is tempted to try again. The amazing thing is that even a one-year-old seems to sense that it isn't right for the parent to be so submissive and that it isn't right for him himself to be able to gain the upper hand so easily. Getting away with meanness to a parent makes him uneasy. When the mother says that the two-year-old chortles with glee, I can't believe that he's really happy. I imagine the child's feelings are a mixture of excitement and guilt. I'll go further and guess that the child is begging for some restraint so that he can truly enjoy playing with his father.

Now the picture that this mother draws is such an unusual one that you may think it hasn't much application for other families. But there are quite a few families in which the mother says, "My main complaint is that my husband leaves every bit of the disciplining of the children to me, even when he's home in the evening and on weekends." There are several excuses that such a father will give: that he's tired at the end of the day, or wants to just relax on weekends, that the mother has to manage the children most of the day anyway, so he doesn't know the rules she wants followed. But these particular excuses don't hold much water. With more justification he may complain that when he tries to participate in the management of the children his wife brushes his directions aside impatiently, or that she often bosses the children unnecessarily and then expects him to back her up. Of course, minor differences of opinion such as these between father and mother occur from time to time in most families, but in the families I am thinking about such complaints are more chronic. Typically, though not always by any means, the mother is the more managerial parent and the

IV

Behavior Problems in

the Young Child

❖❖❖❖❖❖❖❖❖❖❖❖

THE AGGRESSIVE
CHILD

Most cases start with
tensions inside the family.

MOTHERS ASK, "What makes a child aggressive, and what can you do about it?" There are so many different answers, depending on what you mean by the word. What's disturbing aggressiveness to one parent is healthy animal spirit to another.

Students of education and psychology and medicine often ask, "Is aggression normal?" Everyone is endowed with the capacity to become aggressive under the stress of dangers of various kinds or in response to the hostility of others. The gentlest of mothers will attack a dog that is threatening her child. Kind men can be taught to kill in a wartime army where the alternative is to be killed.

Most psychologists would use the term "normal aggression" to include the drive or forcefulness which ordinary people put into such everyday activities as games and business striving. In this sense there is nothing abnormal about aggression, as long as it is not excessive for the situation.

I believe — like most people in the psychological professions and most parents — that children are born with different amounts of drive or aggressiveness, even though this can be modified a lot by the experiences they have later. Mothers will comment on the greater activity of one baby while in the womb, which continued right on through childhood. It's so apparent that one infant is content and docile from the earliest months, another shows his energetic nature and impatience by the time he's a month old — always straining to raise his heavy head on his weak little neck whenever he's awake on his stomach. A couple of months later he's already struggling to pull himself to a sitting position as soon as you take hold of his hands.

It would have been more appropriate to call the docile baby "her" because I have the impression that a larger proportion of the gentle ones are girls.

☙ ☙ ☙

Normal aggressiveness and the exaggerated forms vary at different stages of development. To me, one of the fascinating things about the first and second years of life is that though a baby has occasional rages, all right, he doesn't usually direct them at other people. Even when he's one and a half years of age and knows just whom he's mad at (when his mother deprives him of something breakable or dangerous) he takes it out on himself and the floor by pounding it with his arms, legs, and head. It's as if he has an inborn inhibition against attacking people, which he only gradually overcomes with experience in this harsh world. At six or eight months, when he's miserable with teething and tries to gnaw his crib rail to splinters, he's usually careful not to bite his mother's nipple. If he yields to the temptation occasionally he can, in most cases, be easily inhibited again by a sharp word or other correction. Young kittens and puppies show the same restraint. They love to play at tearing each other and people's hands to pieces, but they're surprisingly careful not to go too far.

A baby experiments delicately with hurting as he gets to be about a year old. Looking his mother straight in the eye during a fretful period, he begins pulling at her hair or slowly approaches her cheek with his mouth open. It's as if he feels the impulses to be mean, but knows that his nature disapproves. A sensible mother promptly reminds her baby that she doesn't like it and that it's not allowed, by pulling back and by restraining his hand or mouth if he tries again. Another mother, who is not quite straight in her feelings and who is willing to play the hurt-and-be-hurt game, *lets* the baby bite and then just looks reproachful, or pretends to whimper. Then the baby, with a slightly sadistic grin, does it a little harder the next time.

You can see that I have a theory that a child under three years doesn't attack very vigorously unless he's encouraged or taught to. Frequently parents complain that their first child at the age of two is incapable of defending himself when other children grab his toys or knock him down. He looks bewildered or cries and runs to his parent. They worry that he's going to be a sissy. By the age of three the parents report, in most cases, that he has learned how to fight back, from bitter experience.

I don't remember ever hearing this complaint about a second child. He has usually taken enough punishment from the jealous first child by fifteen or eighteen months so that he's learned to hang on to his possession like grim death, or whack his brother with it, screaming all the time for whatever help he can get from a parent.

At one or two years of age biting seems to come naturally as a first line of defense or offense, but pushing the opponent over or whacking him with a heavy object is popular too. In other words, the aggression that does come out in earliest childhood is crude and direct. By three or four years of age you begin to see the effects of civilization and maturation. Instead of attacking immediately, kind children will often first ask or explain or protest.

More important still is the turning of aggressive feelings into play form. A child will play the cowboy shooting the bad guy, the giant knocking down the house (made of blocks), the cop (on a tricycle) chasing the robber. You might call such play simply the safety valve for hostility, the blowing off of anger he may have accumulated toward his brother or parent. Yet it's also something more important than that. It's practice in controlling his feelings in accordance with the rules of the grown-up world for which he is already developing respect.

Some conscientious parents get this turned around. They try to discourage gun play in the four-to-eight-year-old period fearing that it might lead to gangsterism or brutality in adult life, whereas it really represents, at this stage, a way station in the progress toward civilization.

The age period between three and six is one in which most children get along relatively well with their parents because they are more aware of how much they love them and want very much to be like them. However, the fact that a boy at this stage normally feels a special romantic and possessive love for his mother — and the girl for her father — makes for an undercurrent of rivalry between boy and father, between girl and mother. In most cases this rivalry does not come to the surface in a dramatic way because the child does his best to suppress it and because the parents maintain a wholesome relationship with each other and with each child, which gives little encouragement to the rivalry. But in a few families where things have got out of balance, the mother may be quite baffled to have her four- or five-year-old daughter become surprisingly antagonistic to her for no apparent reason. (In a similar way during adolescence, which is a stage where rivalry is even more intense, a mother may get the feeling that she's pure poison to her daughter.) The rivalrous antagonism of son to father shows on the surface less frequently because sons seem to be, on the average, more in awe of their fathers than girls are of their mothers.

After the age of eight or nine, the simple play-acting of hostility loses some of its fascination. That's where the comics and

TV and movies come in. Westerns and crime stories give full rein to all kinds of imaginary aggressions, and then subject them to the penalty of the law by the end of the episode.

The age period between about six and twelve years is one in which the child's own maturing nature makes him try to subdue the impulses which he feels are wrong. Open expression of hostility, especially toward the parents, comes under strict control, even in play form. A four-year-old boy can point a pretend pistol at his mother and grin while he tells her he's shooting her dead. But by the time he's nine years old his conscience has become so strict that it makes him step over a crack in the sidewalk when such a thought merely pops into his mind.

In this age period a child no longer feels free to attack a brother or sister without provocation. He may be almost as antagonistic underneath as he used to be. But he works into a fight step by step, subtly provoking his opponent to counterattack, so that he is convinced at each stage that he is only standing up for his rights.

☙ ☙ ☙

Now comes the more complicated matter of what the environment does to change the intensity and the character of aggressiveness. Certainly the most important factor is the fit between the child's nature and the personality of mother and father.

Parents are obliged to adjust to the child they receive as much as he has to adjust to them. Some parents take much more easily to girls, and others to boys. Some have a knack with roughnecks and others are particularly successful in bringing out a naturally cautious, shy child. I've never talked with a mother who didn't find one child more baffling than another.

Often the baby who is overactive to start with tempts his mother to use methods of handling which increase his over-activity. I think of an energetic one-and-a-half-year-old I watched one morning in a park, who occasionally wandered off toward a road or got into other situations which his mother thought dangerous. She kept darting after him and yanking him back to safety. As the morning wore on you could see that he became frantic with her constant restraint and lost interest in everything but an obsession to dash away from her and toward the road. Of course you can see here not only an active child and a restraining mother; there was something a little unwholesome in her willingness to stay in that spot for two hours, letting the situation deteriorate into such a frustrating one for her son and herself.

Freud first made clear that a long-drawn-out toilet-training struggle between mother and child in the period between one and three years can build a lot of antagonism into a child's impressionable character. In a few cases this results in an outwardly aggressive child. More often, the reasonably good relationship that mother and child have established in other respects, and the fact that he values her love and feels guilty in defying her, makes him control his hostility (and eventually his bowels). So he is more likely to end up with a personality that contains an uncomfortable mixture of too much balkiness and too much guiltiness, rather than an openly hostile one.

A mother recently wrote me about the difficulty she's experiencing bringing up her third child, a boy now four years old. Her first two were girls, now twenty-four and twenty-two years old. She found them easy, even fun to raise. She remembers no particular problems at any time at home. Perhaps we should take this with a grain of salt, since time draws a rosy curtain. But they must have been generally well adjusted because they did wonderfully in school and college, academically and socially. In the seventeen years that followed the birth of the second girl, the mother first suspected and then gradually became certain that she wasn't going to have any more children. By the time she was in her forties she was highly satisfied with a life that was filled with social activities and accompanying her husband on business trips to faraway places. They saw their daughters only during vacations and, as most parents of college students know, not too much then. When her doctor told her at forty-two that she was pregnant, she was at first incredulous, then dismayed and resentful. Being a realistic person, she eventually made the adjustments necessary in her thinking and planning. But in her feelings — no matter how much she tried — she never could become enthusiastic about the coming baby, and this added guiltiness to her other troubles. The baby turned out to be one of those very fretful ones who make the most joyful of mothers feel rejected and irritable. As he progressed through infancy it became clear that he was to be the wiry, restless, tireless, insistent kind.

As he got into the more independent stage after a year she found him increasingly mischievous and disobedient. She says she kept after him and tried many forms of discipline, without effect. At four he is said to be overactive, often rude and defiant at home, sometimes destructive to the neighbors' property, and mean to other children. This case has unusual elements, but it's a clear example of the point that children do things to their parents as much as the other way around. I think that the aggressive behavior has been increasing because his mother rubs him the wrong way with her irritability and is prevented by her guiltiness from exerting a consistent control. Anyway, she has decided, wisely, that she needs some professional help. She and the boy should be able to profit from it.

☙ ☙ ☙

Aggressiveness can be stirred up by other family relationships. Most parents with two or more children have seen it stimulated by a small child's jealousy of a new baby. It's especially in children under three years that the hostility is apt to come right out in the open and be directed at the baby in the form of blows or pinches or squeezes. I remember a very clear-cut story of how this hostility can be deflected outside the family. A two-and-a-half-year-old girl was attending a nursery school, an unusual one which took children under the age of three. When her baby brother was born there was no visible hostility toward him at home, but she began immediately to make sudden attacks on the only two children younger than herself in school. When one of them would come within a few yards of her she'd pounce like a leopard and sink her teeth into his arm. An assistant teacher was assigned to stay close to her for a few days just to prevent these attacks, but the teacher's attention would wander sooner or later and the bite would occur again.

Once in a while you see a child becoming temporarily aggressive as a result of extreme pressure arising from outside the home: constant bullying from a neighbor child, for instance, or a severe reading disability in first grade, which will make a boy feel suddenly inadequate, ridiculous, and resentful.

But most cases of aggressiveness start with tensions inside the family and have to be solved by relieving these tensions. In some of these situations the parents are completely baffled as to where the cause lies. In others, they feel that they understand the issues, and yet the remedies they apply don't bring results. The usual explanation is that the most fundamental cause is not apparent and this is where an outside professional person is able because he is not in the thick of things — to help shed light.

The most direct approach to the solution of behavior problems is to consult a child psychiatrist in private practice or a child-guidance clinic, but such facilities are available in only the largest cities and they sometimes have waiting lists. Another approach is to consult a family social agency. (The name of the most appropriate one can be secured through the Community Chest office.) A social worker's training and experience enable her to give mothers the help they need in solving most of these problems. If the social worker finds that a different kind of treatment is needed, she is in a position to assist the mother in finding a psychiatrist or guidance clinic for the job. In the case of school children, there is often some type of counseling service in the school or at the board of education.

THE DAWDLER

The more the child feels pushed,
the more he slows down.

When mothers complain about procrastination in children, the descriptions are often the same. My experience has been that though there are some girl procrastinators, there are a lot more boys. And the parents who are driven mad are more commonly the mothers. Children may show some procrastination in the preschool years, but the problem usually becomes worse in the early school years. So let's take a typical situation: a mother telling about her nine-year-old son.

She starts with the trouble she has in the morning. That's the time when the family needs to hurry most and when the procrastinator is usually at his worst. The mother says she has to go back into his room several times to get him out of bed. Then, while she's making breakfast, she has to keep checking to see whether he's getting dressed. Often he isn't. She reminds him, more and more forcefully, to get going. When it's time for breakfast, she may find him sitting on the edge of his bed, stark naked. Apparently he started, some time ago, to slip one sock on, but froze in that position while he read a comic book.

When he gets to the table he's way behind schedule, but you wouldn't know it from the way he acts. He dreams off and on, and he eats in slow motion. The mother tells him frantically that he'll be late for school or miss the bus, but he doesn't look as if he had heard. If he has brothers and sisters who have to wait for him to start to school, they add their noisy warnings. If they leave without him, he may put on a slight burst of speed at the very last second, or when he sees the school bus arrive.

The situation is repeated at lunchtime. There is difficulty in the afternoon and on weekends if there are chores to be done or appointments to be kept. When the family is going anywhere, everyone else is in the car before this child, calling to him. There's usually trouble at bedtime. A dawdler has to be driven even harder than the average to take a bath, and then he has to be shouted at repeatedly to get out of the bathroom. He may barricade himself in the bathroom for exasperatingly long periods at other times too. If he's a reader at all, he may bury himself in books on all possible occasions, as if they were a refuge from all the pressures of the world.

🎜 🎜 🎜

What makes procrastination? Possibly inborn temperament plays a part, though this has not been proved. Sometimes it starts in the toilet-training period. Many a baby, somewhere between twelve and eighteen months of age, suddenly realizes that his bowel movement, which up to then he has been depositing in the toilet or potty without much thought, is a personal matter, a product of his own body. He discovers it, you might say, as he discovers other parts of his body, and he feels rather proud and possessive about it. He may no longer be so willing to give it up and he may hold it in, at least as long as his mother makes him sit on the seat. If she is very persistent in keeping after him and the movement, he may, with practice, learn to withhold it for hours and even days. He thus acquires the habit of resisting pressure by delaying. If his mother, in exasperation, continues for many months to demand the movement and if he chooses to continue to balk in the same way, the pattern of stalling may become permanent, and spread to other situations besides toileting.

Another child may develop procrastination without going through any visible struggle over toilet training. A combination which seems to favor it is a mother with an energetic, impatient disposition and a child who seems to be deliberate by nature. This causes no trouble during the first year, when no demands are put on a baby anyway. But when he gets to be one and two he is expected to come to the table when it is mealtime and to feed himself, to keep up with his mother when she is walking him to the playground or through the supermarket. This is a slow-moving, attention-wandering age, which puts a strain on any mother's patience. More important, it's an age when the child's nature insists that he develop his independence. He feels that he must assert his dignity and his rights as an individual. He says "No" whenever he sees an issue, even about things he'd like to do. He certainly objects to being bossed in obvious ways. He insists on trying to do things for himself — like putting on shoes — though it's apparent that he doesn't have the skill. If he gets way behind his mother on the sidewalk and she stops and calls him, he's apt to stop, too, though he may pretend not to notice her. If she starts back after him, he may move off in the opposite direction.

The temptation to the parent to prod and get irritated is severe. However, this age period is a lot less trying for some parents than for others. The very easygoing mother is not trying to steer the child all day and she doesn't worry a lot about shaping his character. It's her nature to live and let live, so there aren't too many occasions to tangle with the young rebel. A mother who sails through life on charm and tact enjoys using her ingenuity to get her child to do what she wants him to do. The mother who doesn't feel much obligation to control her own feelings blows up every once in a while when exasperated with her obstinate small child, then feels relieved and lets him alone.

I think it's particularly the parents who have more than average amounts of masterfulness and impatience, and who at the same time are conscientious in trying to control any aggressiveness on their own part, who are most apt to keep pushing their children and thus foster dawdling. Occasionally it's the mother who feels, underneath, critical or rivalrous with men (perhaps as a result of childhood tensions with brother or father) who has the most impatience with her son.

However the trouble starts, when a child dawdles, an impatient parent feels like pushing. The more the child feels pushed, the more he slows down. It's a neat way for him to fight back. He's asserting his right to resist domination. At the same time he gets back at his parents in a way which is *particularly* irritating to them. Yet he doesn't have to take the dangerous course of openly defying the parent (the way a less strictly controlled child might). It's as if he and his parent were both afraid of open hostility, the parent because of conscientiousness and self-control, the child because of fear of losing the parent's love. Instead, they all tacitly agree on a restricted sort of combat which never becomes lethal but which never ends.

彑 彑 彑

Prevention is a lot easier than cure. In the case of the one-and-a-half-year-old who has decided he wants to retain his bowel movement — at least until he is off the seat — the baffled mother may assume she has only two alternatives: to give up her training efforts for an indefinite period, which seems intolerable to her; or to keep the child on the pot for as long as necessary and to exhort him, earnestly or sternly. The second method expresses the mother's feelings better, but the flaw in it is that the frailest child can always beat her at this game. However, there is a third approach. This is to say hopefully to the child each day, when cleaning up the accident, "Maybe tomorrow when you want to do duty, you'll tell mommy and do it like a big boy in the seat." This is not insisting on getting something out of him, but suggesting that someday he'll want to grow up. It won't change his mind right away — nothing will. But it will work sooner than grim insistence. This advice sounds logical enough. But it's hard to carry out for those parents to whom soiling and balking are the most irritating things a child can do.

In the case of the two-year-old who keeps stalling on the way to market, there are several alternatives to urging him to hurry. If the mother keeps moving along, the child will usually follow, despite his stops and his side trips, just as ducklings follow the duck, but this kind of progress is particularly frustrating to some parents. It's more practical to pop him in his stroller and whisk him along, postponing the stroll till another time of day when there is no hurry. Or he might be left with a neighbor.

But suppose that the fat is in the fire, in the sense that the child is now seven or eight years old and a confirmed dawdler. In the age period between six and twelve the child's striving to be more independent of his parents and to run his own life seems to accentuate his tendency to use procrastination as a universal weapon. Besides, the necessity for him to get up, eat breakfast, and get off to school presents a crisis five mornings a week which can't be evaded the way certain troublesome situations can be dodged in the preschool period.

The best strategy I know (and I don't mean it's sure-fire) consists of two parts. The first is for both parents to keep as much in the background as possible, so that the child's own sense of obligation and pride about getting to school on time will have the best chance to motivate him. Parents who have been prodding and threatening for months, with less and less success, will swear that the child has no sense of urgency about getting to school at all. But that isn't usually true. Ninety-nine out of a hundred children who have grown up in a conscientious family are in considerable awe of the rules of school and are quite sensitive to the disapproval and snickering of their classmates. The reason this is not apparent in the case of the procrastinator is that the tug of war with his parents and the turmoil each morning so preoccupy him that he has almost no time to think about school until the last minute.

When it's decided to turn over a new leaf in the family, it's wise to get the fullest benefit from it by a friendly conference. The parent might say, "I've decided that it's foolish for me to keep nagging you every minute about getting up and getting ready for school. It must irritate you and make you want to go slower and slower. It certainly wears me out. I'm going to try and take care of my job and let you take care of yours. I'll just call you once and then let you do the rest." In most cases this won't cause an overnight reformation. In fact, a child who has developed procrastination to a fine point usually has to test his parents to the limit. The first few mornings will be agony for them. The more patient parent will have to give moral support to the impatient one; in fact, may have to restrain him or her by gentle force. The child will probably come hustling downstairs just in time to leave the house. This is success enough for a start. Suppose he misses the bus? I'd let him. I'd be careful not to taunt him, but rather try to be sympathetic ("I guess it's hard to do at first, when you're used to being reminded so often"), since the purpose of the plan is to help him, not to get even with him. If he begs to be driven to school, I'd agree to do it once, but I'd remind him that it won't help him to learn how to run his own life if he has to count on being driven every day.

The hope is that as the days go by and the child becomes convinced that the pressure is off, he will be able gradually to abandon his end of the struggle.

Now for the other part of the program, which may be combined with the first, or substituted for it if the first shows no sign of working. It consists in the parent who is the more patient of the two taking over the management of the dawdler in the situations where procrastination is a problem. Of course this won't work if both parents have been driven equally to distraction, or if the parent who takes over soon finds that his patience vanishes under provocation. But in most families one parent can be much more patient in ignoring the procrastination. By carrying on a chatty conversation, from room to room during dressing, and also at breakfast, the parent may be able to change the morning atmosphere. Is it safe to offer a reward each month for a record of promptness? This may prove to be a trap if it becomes a new excuse for prodding ("Remember, you won't get your reward if you are late"), but I've seen it used with success in the hands of the nonpatient parent, along with other methods.

I have known families in which dawdling at mealtime was so upsetting to one parent that it proved worth while to serve the children's meals separately, inconvenient as that sounds.

If, despite all efforts, the problem persists beyond a reasonable time, the parents had better seek professional help, for their own comfort as well as the child's.

THE WHINER

Child and mother get caught
in a vicious circle.

I THINK whining is most common at about two or three years of age. But I remember a couple of bad cases in babies under a year of age; and a few people are still whining in old age.

Perhaps we should first try to figure out the meaning of the symptom in the two babies, since an infant's psyche is supposed to be less complex. In the first case — a boy — the parents had been overjoyed to have a baby, since they had been waiting for several years. They held him and played with him most of the time he was awake, so I think there was, from the beginning, an element of simple spoiling; he became used to being constantly entertained and lost some of his ability to find his own fun. But then as he got nearer the age of a year, his tendency to stay awake longer and his more advanced interests made him demand fancier entertainment — and for more hours of the day. This began to tax the mother's patience. There was also the factor that as any child grows out of the helplessness of early infancy, the parents' impulse to pamper him and dote on him gradually grows less. If this weren't true, parents would still be talking baby talk to their two- and three-year-olds, chucking them under the chin, feeding them bottles, and carrying them from place to place.

Wherever the baby was sitting, he would be holding up his arms and whining. His mother would try to ignore him, but after a while his fretting would make her feel uncomfortable and conscience-stricken. She'd pick him up and play with him for a few minutes and then try to put him down again. The reaching and whining would start immediately. The mother's endurance wore thin. Underneath, she resented the baby's demandingness. But she was too conscientious — and inexperienced — to recognize her growing antagonism, so she always suppressed it and gave in to him.

I think that a baby as young as ten months will sense his mother's irritation, though she is covering it up, and this makes him both cross and uneasy. The combination stimulates him to demand more attention. He is also quite aware of the power he exerts over her, in the sense that he knows she doesn't feel entitled to stand up to his excessive demands, and this invites him to be more tyrannical too. So child and mother get caught in a vicious circle. He has to keep on badgering her. She can't deny him, but she can't feel friendly toward him either.

The second case is that of an eight-month-old girl whose history was a little more complicated. The parents had been married only a year when she was born, and soon afterward the father was drafted into the Army during World War II. For several months the mother, an anxious person anyway, lived near Army camps, dreading the day when he would be sent overseas. After that happened, since she had no suitable relatives with whom she could stay, she was living a rather shut-in existence with the baby.

The baby had reacted to all the family tension by becoming an unusually anxious as well as demanding creature. She had the expression of a worried, angry, fretful old lady. Her mother had to carry her all day long, and far into the evening, even while she cooked and did the laundry. The baby refused to let a sitter touch her or to let her mother out of her sight, until she finally fell asleep about 10 or 11 P.M. So the mother never got a moment's relief. The whining was sometimes soft and absent-minded and it was sometimes loud and domineering, but it never stopped.

I suspected that the mother had felt an understandable resentment, from the beginning, toward this child who had come so soon and complicated her brief marital life, and she must have strongly resented the increasing tyranny, but she was reluctant to admit this. She gave in to all the baby's demands, without protest.

This second case is more exaggerated than the first, but I think it only brings out more clearly the same pattern seen in so many cases of whining: a child who chronically makes more demands on the mother than she can respond to. She is resentful underneath, but she is too guilty to be able to say no to him. His awareness of her irritation and of his power both urge him on to needle her further.

In a child of two or three or more years, the situation is rarely as drastic. He can get places by himself. He is distracted part of the time by objects and activities around the house and by other children outside. So now we can see all the milder and specialized types of whiner: the one who feels the need of more attention only when his mother gets absorbed in conversation on the street or on the telephone; the rainy-day whiner; the one who is missing a best friend who has moved away; the one who is always saying, "There isn't anything to do," or "What can I do now?"

🖤 🖤 🖤

I think there are two kinds of reactions in mothers, with a certain amount of overlapping. One is highly conscientious and self-disciplined. She manages to preserve a facsimile of a cordial facial expression and patient tone of voice, even after hours of provocation. The other may be made cranky and even angry by the whining, but one can see that she shows no masterfulness in stopping it. So the difference is mainly in the degree of self-control.

I remember, many years ago, when I went on an all-day picnic with another family, being driven nearly mad by the continual whining of their five-year-old son and — even more — by the patient way in which the mother let it go on. She wasn't a wishy-washy or long-suffering person in other relationships. In fact, she was quite a masterful person with her other son and daughter, making them toe the mark for her, being sure that they didn't bother other people. It was clear that there was something out of kilter only between her and the whiner. It kept her from showing any resentment. It kept her answering — with fantastic patience — his senseless complaints and his selfish demands. It was easy to see that these matters didn't really mean much to him in themselves, but that he was cooking them up to pester her. It was quite clear, too, that his whiny relationship was only with her, since he didn't show any of it toward his father, brother or sister.

I've been implying, in these examples, that any mother could quickly stop a child from whining unless she was paralyzed — or blinded — by some kind of guiltiness. I may be exaggerating and oversimplifying a bit — in fact, I'm sure I am — but I'll stick by the statement in a general way. All of us parents have let a child whine at us and nag at us at times. Perhaps we have turned down his request for some excursion or treat or privilege, and then begun to wonder whether we were too hasty. He senses our self-doubt instantly and sets to work on us. Or we have been unfairly disagreeable to a child, perhaps because we were mad at somebody else or ourselves, and then, without realizing what it was all about, allowed him for a while to whine or be rude or be disobedient.

When we are on balance, when we are reasonably sure inside that we love our children enough and are treating them fairly, we manage them easily. Our manner is friendly but firm. This makes them feel agreeable, makes them want to please us. Then when we have to tell them what to do or not to do, it sounds fair to them because there's no buried meanness or guiltiness in our tone. When they start to whine, in hopes we'll give in to some unreasonable request, and we say "None of that whining," they realize, from the assured tone we used, that they might as well save their breath.

So when a child is a chronic whiner, month in and month out, the parent who is looking for a solution should consider the possibility that it's the parent's own unconscious feeling of crossness and guilt which is keeping him from sensibly controlling the child. It's a great pity because these feelings are preventing parent and child from enjoying the mutual fondness to which they are entitled.

It's much more difficult for a parent to find the source of such feelings when they are chronic than when they are just temporary. Their roots may go back to difficulties in the child's infancy, as in the case of the baby who was spoiled by the parent's delight and inexperience. The roots may go farther back, to the parent's own childhood, to some tension between him and his parent or brother or sister. The most appropriate place to turn first for help — as in any kind of family problem that resists solution — is to a family social agency.

Let me return for a moment to my confession of oversimplification. I've been explaining what I think is the most common pattern behind whining. But there are other emotional disturbances which can be expressed by this symptom. There are physical causes too. A good example is celiac disease (sometimes called starch indigestion), a chronic disease starting around the age of one year, which is characterized by loose smelly bowel movements and is usually accompanied by emotional irritability.

So I had better end up by advising that if a child becomes a whiner, the situation should be investigated both physically and emotionally.

THE POOR EATER

A feeding problem is not
a rational matter.

"MY PROBLEM has to do with the one thing that I've found, in my twenty-one months as a mother, looms over the heads of lots of other mothers as the most irritating and long-lasting of the many problems having to do with child raising — that of eating. At just a little past a year of age my son, who had been eating everything and anything that would fit into his mouth, suddenly did a complete turnabout to the point where, today, his entire diet consists of little more than bacon, fruits, and bread. I've heard of babies going on tangents and eating only one particular food for days or even weeks at a time. But this has been going on for more than eight months now, and although he does get his vitamin drops each day, I find myself wondering how long he can remain healthy on such a limited diet.

"What is a mother to do — see that, above all, baby's mealtime is happy and give him only those foods that he likes, or insist (through tears and tantrums) that he at least *taste* something new occasionally?"

I suspect this mother is quoting me — with a touch of irritation and sarcasm — when she says "see that, above all, baby's mealtime is happy and give him only those foods that he likes." I agree that she is in no mood to create a happy mealtime when she's worried sick about a child's meager and lopsided diet. And it isn't just that she's anxious. She can't help being angry. She's bought and cooked and served good food and this tiny, opinionated whippersnapper turns it down day after day. She knows he doesn't have allergies to all these foods, nor an inborn dislike for them, because he was eating them happily only a few months ago.

Her worry is probably not just over his own health and safety, which is bad enough, but what her husband, her mother, the doctor, and the neighbors will say about him as he grows thinner and thinner, and what they'll think about her. He can make a monkey of her just by calmly turning his head away and saying "No," and there's really nothing she can do about it. Though she may feel like grabbing him, shaking him, spanking him, or at least shouting at him indignantly, she knows from trying it or just from a hunch that it will never work — it will only make him worse. The only thing she did, in the beginning, to bring this about was to be a conscientious mother. The guilt she feels for getting so mad, openly or inside, complicates the picture, of course, as time goes on.

I've often said that of all the stages of childhood when feeding problems can begin, the one-to-two-year-old period is by far the worst. Part of the explanation may be the further slowing down in weight gaining that occurs about this time. The average baby gains one and a half pounds a month during the first five months, one pound a month from then till twelve months, and half a pound a month during the second year. You can see that, with all the weight gaining and sleeping, an infant's main job during the first year is to become bigger and stronger. But after the first year physical growth obviously takes a back seat. Now a lot of other things are much more important, such as exploring, learning, asserting. The ravenous appetite of the first year *has* to slack off or he'd turn into a monstrosity.

In some children you can suspect that teething plays a part.

I myself think that the teething that goes on in the first few months of the second year and that produces four molars at about the same time is the toughest teething of all.

But most important of all is the sense of individuality that comes on with such a rush in most children in the second year. They realize that they have wishes that can be expressed, and a dignity to maintain. They not only assert themselves about choices that are important to them, but they make issues over matters about which they really don't give a darn. It's self-assertion for the sake of self-assertion, which seems like pure cussedness to the parent but is an essential step in growing up, if you stop to think of it. If every baby didn't have this compulsion to convince his parents and himself that he's an individual, he'd never become a worth-while person.

But I doubt that the child described in the letter is merely expressing the decreased appetite and the increased willfulness of the average one-year-old. He obviously has developed a strong aversion to most foods. Such a feeding problem may start from the usual one-year-old pickiness, but it has probably also encountered a greater-than-average capacity for worry and irritation on the mother's part. Sometimes the story comes out clearly that the mother was a feeding problem in her own childhood and still remembers her own disgust with food and her mother's anger at mealtimes. Parents who have had a long-lasting problem in childhood — whether it was school difficulty or toilet-training rebellion or sissiness or conflict with the father — sometimes find that, however firmly they've decided to handle such matters more reasonably with their own children, instead they become tense, anxious, angry, and guilty in no time at all. I don't say that this always happens, by any means. But the fact that it occasionally happens shows how powerful the feelings left over from conflicts in our own childhood can be, certainly powerful enough to sweep all reasonable intentions away. (Though I knew I was wrong, I used to get so mad at my son when I thought he was being a crybaby at three and four that he still remembered it twenty years later.)

A one-year-old is plenty old enough to know when his parent is tense. In the case of a feeding conflict, it probably makes his food taste like poison. To understand what I mean, think of some person whose tenseness makes you uncomfortable. Now enlarge him to five times normal size, sit him down beside you (with no one else around to appeal to) and imagine him trying to make you eat foods you dislike and getting angrier all the time. The fact that he may be trying to suppress the anger doesn't make much difference.

᪥ ᪥ ᪥

It helps a mother to be forewarned that appetite is likely to become capricious at about a year, particularly for vegetables and cereal and milk. Fruits and meats usually stay popular, but meats must be ground fine, especially for poor eaters. A lump of meat makes them feel like gagging. But knowing ahead of time about the likelihood of poor appetite doesn't guarantee that a parent can take it in stride.

It's easy enough to tell the mother who wrote me that trying to get a squeamish child to take a taste of other foods won't work, but she really knows that already. She just threw that question in as an expression of her exasperation at his unreasonableness. It should comfort her a little to know that most of us parents have been equally irritated by our children (most often the first).

The most rational approach is to reassure her that though the child's diet is unconventional, it does cover the essentials. Fruits, whole-wheat bread, milk (she doesn't mention milk, but she may be listing only the solid foods), and a multivitamin preparation can constitute a quite adequate diet if the amounts are reasonable. To be sure, it doesn't guarantee that all the requirements are doubly covered, as a more varied diet will, but it's a lot better than children get in many parts of the world. In any such case a doctor or nutritionist should go over the diet, estimate whether any essentials are omitted and suggest substitutes (such as calcium tablets when no milk is being consumed).

She can also be reassured that children who are eating small amounts of the essentials and gaining slowly are not more susceptible to colds and other common childhood infections. But the trouble with attempting to reassure the mother on rational grounds is that a feeding problem is not a rational matter. A skimpy eater, even though he's taking the essentials, still makes a parent anxious.

A word needs to be said about weight gaining in the preschool and early school years. The average is about five pounds a year. This is a small amount spread over twelve months, and it seems even less to a worried parent. Again and again, when I've told a mother the present weight of a child about whose eating she was dissatisfied, she has exclaimed with dismay, "Why, that's just what he weighed six months ago!" In four out of five cases a comparison with the previous weight shows that the mother's impression is wrong and that the child *has* gained two or three pounds. This pessimism is part of the state of mind of the parent of a small eater.

The only way I know to treat a serious feeding problem is to offer the child — for at least three months — only those wholesome foods which he presently enjoys. The first step is to go over, in detail, a list of all the usual foods, looking for the few he likes. If you just ask, "Does he like any meats?" the mother says disgustedly "No!" But if you list them all, you're apt to find that he likes hamburgers or frankfurters. Such a list, even if it contains only five items, is *the* diet (supplemented with vitamins and any other essential mineral if possible). The aim is to let the child enjoy meals for a while. It'll take two or three months for his appetite to begin to pick up. It's not that the parent is meant to begin urging other foods after three months, but that the child's stomach may begin asking for them.

I am sure this works if the mother can stick with the doctor and discipline herself, but it's hard work for her. The worst feeding problem I ever heard of was a two-and-a-half-year-old girl who couldn't stand the sight or smell of *any* food or drink while she was awake. In fact, she became terrified when meal-time approached. But she would drink her bottle in her sleep. In order to follow the principle of offering no food she didn't enjoy, it was necessary to omit any food in the daytime and to give her two bottles of milk, fortified with eggs, cereal, cream, vitamins, in her sleep. In two months she was begging for food and in three months eating well.

BED–WETTING

*The sympton is less important than
the underlying disturbances.*

I want to take up in this chapter the difficult topic of bed-wetting (medically termed "enuresis"), dealing in a brief way with the commonest types and causes.

Most children become dry at night between two and three years of age. A few should probably be given the benefit of the doubt until three-and-a-half or four. A small number become dry before two. Rarely, a baby — usually a girl — will become dry by one year of age, before the mother has made any effort at all to train the child in the daytime. This is the clearest proof that night dryness comes naturally, as part of growing up, and not primarily because of the parents' efforts.

There are a number of different reasons for bed-wetting. Some cases are caused by a physical abnormality or disease. Usually in these cases the child has difficulty controlling his urine in the daytime, too (for instance, there may be dribbling every few minutes, which the child can't control, or difficulty starting urination or inability to empty the bladder completely), or there may be burning on urination, frequency, and pus in the urine. Certainly any child who has any urinary symptoms in the daytime or who isn't becoming dry at night by three years should be checked by the doctor.

But in a majority of cases of bed-wetting no physical trouble is found and the child has normal control in the daytime (though he may wet his trousers a bit because he puts off going to the bathroom too long).

Of these cases of psychological enuresis there is still a variety of causes. One of the commoner, though not the commonest, types is the two- or three-year-old who has been dry for a number of months and then begins wetting again when a new baby arrives. He is feeling insecure for a while and, as we all do in such a mood, he retreats to a more babyish state of mind and behavior. He may not only wet his bed, but he may suck his thumb more or cling to his mother's apron strings. Unconsciously he may long to have his mother change his wet night clothes the way she changes the baby's diapers. Perhaps he may also wet — unconsciously in his sleep — because he's mad at her for bringing this baby into his Garden of Eden. When London children were moved to the country in large numbers, at the beginning of World War II, away from family, friends and familiar surroundings, many of them, even adolescents, reverted to bed-wetting. The main cause here, too, was probably retreat to babyhood in sleep, because of insecurity.

The treatment in such cases is to try to make the child feel confident again about his place in the family and in the parents' affection. Since he will surely feel ashamed about his wet bed, even if he doesn't show this on the surface, it's wise to assure him sympathetically that he will soon be able to stay dry again.

☙ ☙ ☙

But the commonest type of enuresis is different still. Four out of five cases occur in boys, and it is the boys that I will discuss first. Most of them have never become really dry at night.

They go on wetting fairly steadily till six or eight or ten or twelve years of age. Often there was more than average difficulty getting the child trained in the daytime, at one and two years, with the mother becoming pretty cross at times and the boy resisting her efforts.

Child psychiatrists who have studied these cases (the late Dr. Margaret Gerard did pioneer work on the problem) believe that in a majority of them — not all — there is tension between the mother and the son. In the most typical case the mother has a strong personality and is critical by nature. She is close to her son and devoted to his welfare. But she tends to be impatient about roughness, noisiness, cockiness, messiness in her son — aspects of boyhood which other mothers can take more philosophically. The boy is of a sensitive make-up, the kind who is easily scared and overawed. He may have become quite dependent on his mother in early childhood, been timid in many situations, and had frequent bad dreams. He is not able to brush aside his mother's disapproval, as so many sons can do; he is too readily convinced that he is immature and inadequate. Seen through his eyes, his mother appears to be a rather overpowering and angry person.

Yet he does not become a docile child, in order to avoid more trouble. He learns to get a subtle, perverse kind of pleasure out of his mother's crossness when she is upset with him, and unconsciously sets out to provoke her in small irritating ways. Though he learns to enjoy submission, at moments, he is also afraid of it and fights against it. His basic problem would be defined by a psychiatrist as a deep conflict between the unhealthy desire to submit passively and the wholesome desire to be active and effective.

An enuretic boy of this kind does not really wet the bed because he has not learned to be dry or because his bladder is too full or because he sleeps too soundly. The bed-wetting occurs each night in a dream in which he is under the power of or at the mercy of some person or animal or natural force. His feeling in the dream is usually a combination of anxiety and pleasure. So you can say that the wetting is a response to a specific kind of excitement. (We once had a female puppy who would get very excited when we came home, roll over into a submissive position on her back, and flood the floor.) In a more general way, enuresis also expresses two other unconscious attitudes in a boy: his sense of being a baby still and his babyish defiance of a mother who is, he feels, too controlling and disapproving.

I want to make it absolutely clear at this point that the boy is not aware of these troubled feelings that are hidden in his mind, or of their connection with his enuresis. Consciously he is very ashamed of his bed-wetting and is usually making strenuous efforts to control it. It would be a mistake and would work in the wrong direction if the parent were to act as if the boy could stay dry if he wanted to. He can't change his dreams any more than you or I can.

If the basic problem with this type of bed-wetting boy is that he feels incompetent and is unconsciously provoking his mother to dominate him, you can see why some of the control methods that conscientious parents use don't work well. Getting him up at night and leading him, stumbling, to the toilet? This is another proof that he can't take care of himself and that the parents have no confidence in him in this respect. Making him wash his own sheets and hang them out in public? Even more humiliating. He is terrified that outsiders, especially the other boys, will find out about his shame. Restricting fluids in the evening? It sounds logical enough, but actually the warning only gives him an immediate thirst — as it would you or me. Then he keeps begging for a drink and the mother has to keep impatiently denying him. This is bad for him and bad for her. Camp? Only if a boy has found that he can usually stay dry away from home and wants to try it himself; and then only if the camp counselors are mature and experienced enough to be able to understand the boy's problem and be ready to protect him. A mediocre camp can be torture for an enuretic.

⚑ ⚑ ⚑

What can be done in a constructive direction? Though the bed-wetting seems like the real problem — to child and parents — it is not the most important one in the long run. In a great majority of cases the enuresis itself ceases before or by the time a boy gets into adolescence. The underlying disturbances — the sense of inadequacy, the conflict about passivity, the temptation to provoke — are not so easily outgrown. Intensive psychoanalysis, several days a week, offers the best chance of getting at the roots of these; next best would be once-a-week treatment in a child-guidance clinic. These forms of therapy are particularly desirable when a boy's personality disturbance is serious enough to cause constant tension with members of the family, nightmares and daytime fears, timidity or provocativeness with other boys.

Parents ask about the electrical apparatus that can be bought or rented which rings a bell and flashes a light the moment the bed is wet. It gradually teaches the boy to inhibit the wetting, in a certain percentage of cases, at least temporarily. As you can imagine, most child psychiatrists would not feel satisfied with a method which suppresses the symptom without getting at the underlying cause at all. Would it do any harm? I suspect it would do no harm and perhaps do some good for a boy who was pretty well adjusted, who was eight years old or more, and who participated in the decision to try it. He could understand what it was all about and, if it removed his symptom, this by itself would improve his self-confidence. It would still leave the basic personality problem. I think that an electrical apparatus might be harmful when used for a young, immature, fearful child. Even if it scared him out of his symptom, it might implant new morbid ideas.

Whether or not they can secure psychiatric treatment, there are certain cues for the parents. They can avoid belittling, express confidence that the boy will be able to gain control of his bladder sooner or later, look for opportunities to foster his confidence in himself. If his mother has been keeping after him about his enuresis she might dramatize the fact that she is turn-

ing over a new leaf in a friendly talk with him: "I think I've
been barking up the wrong tree in keeping after you about the
bed-wetting. It must have irritated you a lot. I understand now
that quite a lot of boys have this problem, but that they practically all manage to gain control of their urine sooner or later.
I imagine you'll get there sooner working by yourself. Good
luck." The parents can try hard not to badger the boy about
the dozens of small issues that come up every day, though this
will be difficult at first because of his irritating ways. They
should still hold him in line about important matters. They can
look for opportunities to build him up in school and in the
neighborhood, seeing to it that he has a bicycle or football if
that's what all the other kids have (rather than holding these
back as an inducement to become dry), making his friends
welcome, fixing up excursions and treats for them occasionally.

We've come to realize through psychiatric work with children
that when they sleep in the room with parents or just beyond
a thin wall, they may be awakened and troubled by the sounds of
intercourse, more often than parents suspect. The personality
make-up of the enuretic boy makes him especially liable to draw
alarming conclusions from what he hears. Therefore it's wise to
have his bed well out of earshot, if this is possible to arrange.

Often in the family of an enuretic boy the father is a quiet
type who, on the one hand, prefers not to take much part in
discipline but, on the other hand, is irritated by his son's imma-
turity and insufficient manliness. Both attitudes make it harder
for the boy to gain confidence in himself. Every boy is helped
to become manly by patterning himself after a father who is
pally with him at times and yet who doesn't hesitate to assert
himself to a reasonable degree in family affairs, especially in the
disciplining of the children. (See "The Father's Role in
Discipline," page 113.)

ᙏ ᙏ ᙏ

What about psychological enuresis in a girl? In the most typical case (and of course there are other kinds) she is not timid or lacking in self-confidence. Quite the contrary. She is apt to be spunky, assertive, perhaps tomboyish. She may be inclined to be quite rivalrous with brothers if she has them, and with other boys. Far from being too distant from her father, she may be unusually close to him. She may want to share all his interests and perhaps dreams of doing his kind of work when she grows up.

If we can say that the problem of the typical enuretic boy is that he feels he is a baby, the problem of the most typical enuretic girl is that she is unconsciously trying too hard to be a boy. If this is her trouble, she will be helped most if both her parents show that they particularly enjoy and love her just because she is a girl. She needs her father's continuing friendliness, but it will actually help her to be happy as his daughter if she sees clearly from his manner that he gives his companionship and tenderness primarily to his wife. His wife plays her part by being receptive to him in these respects.

BEDTIME PROBLEMS
AROUND THE AGE OF TWO

They are almost always based
on separation anxiety.

❄❄❄❄❄❄❄❄❄❄❄❄❄❄❄❄❄❄❄❄❄❄❄❄❄❄❄❄❄❄❄❄

THE BEDTIME problems in children around the age of two, which I want to discuss in this chapter, are quite different from those in babies under the age of one year. The first-year problems fall largely into the category of spoiling, and usually can be cured quickly by parental firmness. But in a one-and-a-half- and two-year-old, the bedtime problems are almost always based on some degree of anxiety in the child — a degree that can range from mild to severe.

The typical story of a very anxious child might go as follows: A mother of a two-year-old boy, an only child, had to go away for a couple of weeks, unexpectedly, and left the child at home in the care of a stranger. When the mother telephoned long distance to hear how things were going, the report was that the child was behaving well, apparently not missing the mother. Actually, a careful comparison with the child's usual behavior showed that he was being too good — letting the stranger feed him, dress or undress him, toilet him, take him outdoors or bring him in, put him to bed without any of the balking and fussing that he often put on for his mother.

But when his mother came home at last, his fearfulness erupted onto the surface like a volcano. He watched her and stuck close to her. If she went out of the room he cried out and ran after her. He wouldn't let the woman who had been caring for him come anywhere near. At bedtime he clung to his mother so tightly that it was almost impossible to get him into bed, and when she started for the door he, who had never even tried to climb out of his crib before, vaulted over the side, picked himself up off the floor and rushed after her. His panic was so heart-rending that his mother didn't try to get away again, but sat by his crib waiting for him to go to sleep. But he stayed awake for about two hours, each night. If his mother tried to steal out before he was fast asleep, he'd stay vigilantly awake even longer.

When behavior like this goes on for days, it's clear that the child is badly upset. The mother is unhappy for the child. At the same time she can't help becoming frustrated at having a child cling to her like a shadow all day and imprison her in his room every evening. This is a picture of what is called separation anxiety, in a quite severe form, and it accounts for some of the most difficult sleep problems in one- to three-year-olds. It's rarely as severe as this, however. Separation anxiety of this degree is usually seen in an only child with an unusually devoted, somewhat overprotective mother. They have always been very close to each other, dependent on each other, and some of the mother's apprehensiveness about what might happen to her child has got through to him.

When I wonder why it is that children right around the age of two are more subject to separation anxiety, I can only guess that they are now old enough to realize how much their parents mean to them but not old enough to be reassured by explanations. A mother says she will be back in a few days. But what can these words mean to a child who hasn't experienced separation before? Her absence for a day probably seems like eternity.

There is very little time sense at this age. A child doesn't even know whether it's morning or afternoon until he's four or five years old.

Now let's turn to a very mild and common type of bedtime problem. Many children around 1¾, 2, 2¼ who have always before gone to bed like lambs and, you might say, gone out like lights, begin to try to keep the mother in the room. "Wanta go wee-wee"; then "Want a drink of water"; then wee-wee and water again. A mother is always in a quandary when wee-wee is mentioned because she has been encouraging the child to become responsible and she doesn't want to seem unco-operative, no matter how sure she is that this is a false excuse.

Another form of two-year-old reluctance to be left in bed occurs when a child learns to crawl out of his crib and quietly appears at the parent's side in the kitchen, dining room, or living room. A child of this age may be unsophisticated in most respects, but he certainly can be very suave in laying on the charm at such a moment, when he knows he's doing something forbidden. He smiles ingratiatingly, he asks friendly questions, he's willing to be cuddly for five times as long as he would be in the daytime. He's irresistible.

I think that the excuses to hold the mother in the room and the slipping out of bed to join the parents are probably signs of a very slight separation anxiety — not caused by any dramatic disappearance of the parent, but rather by the fact that the child is at a developmental stage when it's easy for him to feel loneliness on separation.

Mild and moderately severe separation reactions occur at this age when another relative who has been living in the house leaves, or even when the family moves from one house to another.

🌿 🌿 🌿

What to do? There's no doubt in my mind that if a child is acutely anxious at bedtime, especially if there has been a cause in a parent's disappearance, he has to be thoroughly reassured over a period of weeks. It's important that the mother not go away again until he shows he can take it. At bedtime I think it's best for her to sit by his crib, perhaps hold his hand if he wants that. It doesn't work well to take him in her lap because he will almost certainly wake up when she tries to put him to bed later. It's necessary for her to sit there until he is thoroughly asleep. If she tries to sneak out when he's half asleep, the slightest creak of the floor boards will wake him and then he'll fight off sleep even harder, for fear of her going. It's apt to take a couple of hours the first few nights, which is a terrible chore for any mother. She should make herself as comfortable as possible, read or sew by a shaded light if she likes. If all goes well, the wakefulness will soon be cut down to half an hour, though the half hour of sitting may have to be continued for a couple of months.

Needless to say, I'd get help from a child psychiatrist or a child-guidance clinic, if possible, for a child who was this anxious.

Prevention is easier than cure. If a trip out of town can be postponed for a few months (as in the case of a vacation trip for the parents) until an only child is past two and a half years, there will be less chance of severe anxiety because explanations will have more meaning. If the mother's trip or hospitalization can't be postponed, then it's worth while getting the child accustomed to the woman who will care for him by gradual degrees, over a couple of weeks, if possible. She should first just be around the house and then participate in his care only after he is showing friendliness and confidence. Later his mother can leave the house for a few hours at a time so that he can learn that reappearance follows disappearance. This gradualness gives the woman a chance to see just how the mother handles him too.

Such drastic precautions may not be so important in the case of later children in the family, or even a first child who is unusually independent. When there are several children, they get some of their security from one another. Besides, a mother is apt to outgrow the overprotectiveness she felt toward her first child and to treat the others a little more casually.

In a general way it's good for all children to be familiar with outsiders from the time they are walking and to have the experience, from time to time, if possible, of being left for a few hours with a suitable relative or a tried-and-true sitter. This helps a child gain independence. And it's certainly good for parents to get away from it all occasionally. Of course, the parents must be sure that any sitter is reliable. In the case of a very young child, it's even more important that the mother be certain that a sitter has the right combination of kindliness and sensibleness. A child should be really acquainted with his sitter or sitters. When the parents are going out for the evening the sitter should come before the child is put to bed so that he knows what the situation will be. It's alarming to a small child to wake in the night and find a stranger, or even to find a familiar sitter, when he expects his parent. Accustoming a child to carefully selected outsiders has particular value, of course, when he is the first or only one and when the mother senses that she herself has a tendency to overprotect him.

☙ ☙ ☙

But we haven't discussed the practical management of the very common mild anxieties that make two-year-olds try to keep their parents in their bedroom or climb out of their cribs as soon as the door is closed. In these cases I don't think that the parents should sit with the child or lie on an adult bed beside him. Even hesitancy on the mother's part in saying good night works in the wrong direction. Such parental concern or over-concern will sometimes turn a very mild anxiety into a greater one. In a sense, the child is saying, "I'm beginning to think it may be dangerous to be left alone here. What do you think?" And the mother, by looking uncertain or slightly worried, by falling in with the child's delaying actions, by letting him come into the living room and stay awhile, is answering, in effect, "I don't feel quite right about leaving you alone either. Perhaps there is something to be afraid of." The mother's slight anxiety reflects the child's and increases it a bit. This and his success in pressuring her stimulate him to try harder. The more insistent he becomes, the more hesitant becomes his mother.

A breezy, masterful kind of mother will occasionally report to a doctor, as an afterthought during a two-year-old routine visit, "By the way, a month ago he began trying to stall me at bedtime with the drink-and-bathroom business, but I told him that he'd just had both and I didn't want any of that nonsense. That was the end of that." I'm not necessarily recommending that you use this mother's exact words, but I think you can see that with her manner she is saying, "I'm not in the least bit nervous and you shouldn't be either."

This same kind of firm reassurance can be given to the child who has climbed out of bed to join parents in the kitchen, by *promptly* whisking him back to bed, without succumbing to his wiles for a minute, *every* time.

Parents hearing this idea sometimes say, "That sort of firmness might have worked if I'd thought of it months ago, but the fat's in the fire. Now my child climbs out of bed and leaves his room twenty-five times over a period of two hours — every single night."

I agree that it's much harder to overcome such a pattern once it's well established. But we can get a clue to what might work by asking such a parent, "How do you get him to stay in bed after the twenty-fifth time?" The usual answer is, "Finally I get so mad that I shout at him or spank him. Then he cries a minute and falls asleep." It's not that I think that a shouting or a spanking is the best way to send a small child to sleep. But the twenty-five visits to an increasingly angry parent are not good for a child either. The real point is that the parent should try to be as firm and emphatic the very first time as he has been getting on the twenty-fifth. If he can be that decisive in the beginning — really convince the child that he means business — he won't have to become so angry.

This question of whether the parent really means business and shows the child that he means it is one of the trickiest aspects of child care. All parents *think* they mean it when they tell a child to behave. But an outsider can sometimes see that a parent is only half trying. He may seem very firm and sincere, but at the crucial moment he weakens or loses interest and fails to follow through. We all have our moments when for unconscious reasons we let a child get away with something we officially disapprove of. But in a few parents the inconsistency is extreme. You see them shouting at their children in a blustery way all day long without ever making the slightest real effort to make it work.

To try to make this business clear to a parent who says he has tried but can't make his child stay in bed, I'd ask an exaggerated hypothetical question: "Suppose he were suffering from active heart disease or brain concussion or a broken leg and the doctor said it was vitally important to prevent him from getting out of bed. Could you keep him there?" Of course he could.

While I'm emphasizing firmness I should remind you again that we're now discussing the child with only the mildest kind of anxiety, expressed in delaying tactics and social visits to the parents, not the child who is visibly frightened.

Parents who are desperate ask about locking the child's door. It doesn't seem right to me to give the child the feeling that there is such a barrier between him and them and to run the risk of giving him a fear of being closed in. As a compromise when all else failed, I have suggested a few times, with considerable misgivings, a net covering the top of the crib. The only kind that is available in most cities (in sporting-goods stores) is a badminton net. It is too long and narrow to fit, but it can be cut in two and the two pieces sewed side by side. It must be bound very securely to the back railing and part way across the head and foot of the crib. The front half has to be left unbound, to put the child in. After he is in, the front half is tied to the springs, way under the middle of the mattress, and to the head and foot so that he cannot pry open a hole to climb out through. I would not threaten the child with such a net, as if it were a punishment, but explain that it makes a cozy house for him to sleep in, and let him pretend to help tie it on in the first place. In most cases a two-year-old accepts such a net quite reasonably and after a little calm experimenting settles down to sleep. If he acted frightened I wouldn't use it for even fifteen minutes. I wouldn't even try it for a child over two and a half because of the greater likelihood of a fear of being shut in.

When parents ask me about graduating a two-year-old from a crib — often because a baby is coming along — I always recommend keeping the child in it for another year if he fits, and getting a second one for the baby. I've heard too many stories of two-year-olds becoming wanderers just as soon as they got into a bed without sides.

There's one other important question. Do you let a small child into your bed in the middle of the night when he appears in your bedroom? It certainly seems the easiest thing to do at the time. But in the long run I think it almost always proves to be the wrong answer.

In a great majority of cases the child comes more and more regularly, for more of the night, and the longer it goes on, the more dependent he becomes on it. It gets to be a nuisance to the parents, and most professionals believe that such an arrangement is not wholesome for the child even in the cases where the parents do not mind. So I'd promptly, firmly, and invariably bring such a child back to his own bed. I'd try to avoid staying with him in his own room; but if that was the only way of making him stay put, I'd do it for a few minutes. I wouldn't get in bed with him if he had an adult bed.

V

Attachments and Anxieties
Between Three and Six

❦❦❦❦❦❦

THE MEANING OF FEARS

*The significant emotional developments take place
below the surface, in the unconscious levels of
the child's mind.*

HERE ARE brief excerpts from eight different letters, about children between three and six years of age.

1. "This child is so frightened of dogs I can't get her to go out to play. She just screams and gets petrified when one comes anywhere near her. Her heart pounds so hard you can feel it when you put your arms around her. As far as we know, no dog has ever harmed her."

2. "Will you consider writing on nightmares in preschool children? My 3¾-year-old son has nightmares quite often."

3. "Often she's awake for a couple of hours after going to bed, calling out that she can't go to sleep, asking that her daddy or I lie down with her, etc. When we come upstairs later, no matter how carefully we close our bedroom door, she's awake in an instant, calling out to us to leave our door open."

4. "He can't get his mind off broken things. I never realized how many broken things we had in the house until he pointed

them out. I keep explaining to him how it happened and how it doesn't matter, but he keeps on worrying just the same."

5. "His only anxieties seem to be fear of the dark and a horror of Smokey, the fire-fighting bear. This fear is carried to the point where he will dash out of the living room during station breaks on television, just on the chance that Smokey might flash on the screen. . . . During the past year he has been masturbating a lot."

6. "In children, how do you stop sex play? How can you make them understand that sex is only for adults, and not for children?"

7. "I'll never forget the time at about three and a half years of age when she was sitting on the lap of a casual friend of ours named Arnold and said conversationally, to the room at large, 'Arnold has a penis.' Since it sounded like 'peanuts' she was asked to repeat herself! Thank heavens for understanding friends!"

8. "Lately she has become increasingly obstinate and defiant toward me. She will stand there with her eyes flashing and tell me that she doesn't have to do what I ask. Something has gone wrong which I don't understand. I feel that I must have failed. . . . Her daddy can do no wrong. She not only co-operates with him beautifully but she has taken to mothering him, to his great amusement."

Of course I don't know the full situation in any of these cases because I have only the letters. But they remind me of similar problems in other cases which have been carefully studied in doctors' offices or child-guidance clinics, and which have been found to be related to the complicated pattern of emotional development which children must go through between three and six years of age. Most children manage to navigate this passage on a fairly even keel. Others get stuck on various shoals along the way, or at least are shaken up by the waves, as the examples in the letters indicate.

It's not an easy stage of emotional development to explain. One reason is that it's complicated. But a more important reason — by far — is that the whole description sounds unfamiliar, unlikely, and unwholesome to most adults who have not studied children professionally. The more significant emotional developments take place below the surface, in the unconscious levels of the child's mind) That's one reason why we, as grown-ups, don't recall such feelings and events from our own pasts. They were repressed into our unconscious minds — just as they are repressed into our children's unconscious minds — because they were too disturbing.

Somewhere around three years of age a child is apt to begin to show a more intense affectionateness toward his mother and father. When he was younger he loved them very much, but that was primarily a dependent love. You might say he *had* to love them, because he sensed that he needed them desperately for the security which only they could provide.

Now he is a real person who sees lovable qualities in another real person — and responds to these with delight and devotion. He wants, on his own initiative, to do things for the parent, and to be like the parent.

Another aspect of the three-year-old's love is that it begins to distinguish more sharply between man and woman. The boy sees that he is a male and he will grow to be a man like his father. So his love of his father takes on increasingly the quality of admiration. He watches him carefully and does his best to model himself after him, in pursuits and manner.

His love of his mother, on the other hand, takes on an increasingly romantic quality, partly because of his sexual make-up, partly because of his identification with his father. He wants to regard and treat his mother as his father does.

The little girl now senses that she is on the way to becoming a woman. Increasingly she takes on her mother's interests in child or doll care, housework, feminine adornment. She shows that her feeling toward her father is a special and delightful one just because he is a man. She may play up to him in a coy way that he can't resist.

Between the ages of three and four, most children gain the realization that marriage is the most significant relationship between a man and a woman. In their intense desire to identify with their parents, they begin to think and talk and play marriage. What is not logical to an adult, though very logical to a child, is that he should most often think of himself as marrying that member of the opposite sex who is a hundred times more important to him than any other — his mother if he's a boy, her father if she's a girl. There are many things about marriage which the child doesn't know at this tender age, including the fact that marrying a parent is out of the question. But a sensible mother doesn't shame a child who speaks of marrying her someday, because she senses the devotion and innocence that make such a remark possible. Dozens of parents have told me how patiently they tried to explain to their son that he would grow up and find a lovely girl his own age, only to have him say firmly at the end. "I'm going to marry mommy." When we talk to a small child about finding someone else later, it must sound as preposterous and disloyal and silly to him as it would if we tried the same speech to a newly engaged couple.

Children's romantic and sexual interests are not directed only toward their parents. In fact, the specifically sexual feelings may show up more clearly in relation to other children. They are apt, on one occasion or another when away from adult supervision, to get involved in childish sex play — taking down their pants to show and compare and touch, or "playing doctor." Most of them do at least a little playing with their own genitals. A boy may lean against a lady visitor's knee while talking to her, or ask his mother to touch his penis during his bath. In well-adjusted children these manifestations are not so intense or so sharply focused as in adolescents and adults; and they are fairly easily inhibited — temporarily at least — by the parent. When masturbation or sex play is very persistent, despite parental disapproval, it is usually a sign that the child is anxious or otherwise disturbed.

Another development is a great interest in where a baby comes from, and a desire to have one. There are probably several factors that contribute to this preoccupation. There is now an intense intellectual curiosity about the meaning of *everything* the child runs up against, from where the rain comes from to why birds eat worms. More importantly, his strong identification with parents will make him want to have a baby of his own, just to be like them. He also, at this affectionate age, longs to have a baby to cherish because his parents' love has meant so much to him.

☙ ☙ ☙

Now we should take up a quite different aspect of sexual development in the three-to-six-year-old period: the common and perhaps universal misunderstanding about the physical difference between boys and girls. This is hard for most of us adults to understand. We would assume — from our grown-up logicalness — that when a little boy first saw a girl undressed and realized that she was made differently, he would simply come to the conclusion that this must have been intended by Nature, that all boys must be made one way and all girls another. But the investigations of psychiatrists, beginning with Freud, and the observations of parents show that this fact of life is not learned so simply. Instead, the little boy assumes that everybody was originally made as he was. Therefore he reasons that some injury must have happened to the girl. Then he reaches the further assumption that if something awful could happen to her penis, perhaps it could happen to his.

Girls usually make the same misinterpretation. The principal difference is that the feeling left in the boy is mainly anxiety about future harm; in the girl the anxiety about her incompleteness is mixed with disappointment with her mother for not having made her right and a lingering rivalry with boys because of their presumed advantage. (A few boys, however, become so worried that they envy girls for having nothing to lose.)

Why this tendency in both boys and girls to come to a wrong conclusion which is threatening, instead of to a sensible one which would be reassuring? We know several partial answers. The young child is possessive in a very simple way, tending to want anything he sees. So a little girl seeing a penis thinks it is better to have one, without any more sensible reason. (In the same way a little boy who has just been told that only girls can grow babies in their abdomens is apt to insist vehemently that he is going to grow one, too, no matter what anyone says.)

Early childhood is a period when fears are picked up easily. Perhaps Nature intends it that way on general principles: since there are real dangers in the world, maybe it's safer in the long run if the young child, with little experience to go on, develops too many fears rather than too few. And the ready capacity of the three-, four-, five-year-old to identify himself with others — to feel as he imagines they feel — which is built strongly into him, to foster his learning and his maturation, makes him too sensitive in many situations where he has no basic knowledge to go by. You may have observed, yourself, how easily a three-year-old is upset by death or a cemetery or a cripple. I remember the story of a four-year-old boy who was looking at a picture of a man in an iron lung. He suddenly cried in a panic, "I can't breathe." Just a few seconds of looking at a picture of somebody else had made him imagine the full impact of a paralysis of the muscles of respiration.

Another factor which may contribute specifically to anxiety about the genitals is the kind of warnings which some parents use to discourage masturbation. Nowadays, sensitive mothers and fathers usually avoid punitive threats. But some of them, unable to shake off all the teachings of their own childhood, still speak — however gently and unaccusingly — about the possibility that touching the genital will make it sick or sore. Though such warnings are not drastic in themselves, they readily fit in with other frightening ideas which the child has picked up or imagined. Furthermore, you'd be surprised at the number of parents today who put no stock in modern theories, and angrily threaten that the penis will fall off or that they will cut it off unless masturbation stops.

There's one other important factor contributing to anxiety about genitals, but I'll postpone it for a minute while I trace further what happens to the young child's love of parents. Human love across the sexes always has a possessive aspect. A good man who loves his wife wants her to love only him in this respect, and becomes jealous if another man threatens the relationship. As the small boy's special love for his mother increases, he becomes more aware of the fact that she already belongs to his father. They go out together, they share interests which he cannot understand, they have the same room. The boy slowly faces the fact that he is very definitely second fiddle. This is a bitter realization at any age. It must be extra hard for a small child because he feels outclassed in so many respects — size, strength, smartness, seniority. A boy's resentment extends to his father's genital too. I've been told by a number of fathers that on occasions when they were undressed their sons of four or five made half-joking, half-fierce gestures of grabbing at them.

Probably the reason the boy shows a particular resentment of his father's genital is that it is such an appropriate symbol of the unfairness of their rivalry. He feels like injuring it. Then he jumps to the assumption that his father would like to retaliate. Such reasoning is based on several childish beliefs: that a bad wish is almost as harmful as a bad act; that his parents know all his thoughts; and that if he has angry feelings toward someone, the latter automatically has the same feelings toward him. In the same way, the boy assumes that since he would sometimes like to banish his rival, his father would naturally like to banish him too.

You can see, then, how the child's fear of retribution from his father adds one more to his reasons for being anxious about the safety of his own genital.

Sadly and paradoxically, one of the symptoms which may appear, when a boy becomes excessively worried about his penis, is a preoccupied handling of it. He doesn't seem aware of what he is doing. It is as if he were absent-mindedly reassuring himself that it is still there, and protecting it. This may lead the parents, in their concern for his character and reputation, to make gentle or harsh threats of the harm this might do, which compounds the problem. A girl who is unusually anxious may express it in constant handling too.

A girl feels rivalrous because she realizes that her mother already possesses her father and has had babies by him. She would like to displace her mother in both these respects. (Occasionally this pops out in a happy family when the little girl sweetly urges her mother to go away for a long, long trip, during which time she herself promises to take good care of her father.) But she assumes that her mother knows her mean wishes and that her mother feels quite rivalrous toward her in return. So, in addition to her earlier disappointment that her mother apparently did not try to make her body right in the first place, she may get another idea, that her mother has taken away her penis as punishment for rivalry.

☙ ☙ ☙

You may well be skeptical that such morbid feelings occur. They do not often appear on the surface, especially in happy families. For one thing, it should be remembered that at the very time this rivalry is developing the child is also forming a particularly strong admiration for the parent of the same sex as his or her ideal, and affection for this parent as a delightful companion. This conflict of feelings tends to keep the antagonism out of sight most of the time.

The psychiatrist, who is trying to find out where a child is mixed up, in order to straighten him out, has the best opportunity to see the negative feelings. Over a period of time he creates a favorable atmosphere by refraining from expressing criticism of the child's thoughts, no matter what they are. The child's suppressed impulses begin to come to the surface. He or she draws picture stories and makes up plays with puppets and dolls. In some of these imaginary situations boys kill fathers and fathers come back to life and kill sons or send them to jail. Penises are whacked off with swords. Mothers go away on trips and get wrecked, daughters take over the premises and have babies. Mothers come back to punish.

Though the child's feelings of rivalry, hostility, and fear are repressed into his unconscious, they have a way of reappearing, in disguised forms, in dreams and during the daytime, too, quite apart from the psychiatrist's office. We believe that this is the reason why lots of children have nightmares between the ages of three and six, and why there are many phobias at this time, mild or severe, which have no rational explanation. The fear about injury to his own genital is too intense for the child to tolerate consciously, but it can be expressed indirectly as a preoccupation with broken objects, or as a very exaggerated, anxious curiosity about the genitals of other children, or as a constant absent-minded holding of his own penis, or as a phobia about amputees or other cripples.

The girl's antagonism toward and fear of punishment from her mother can be symbolized in repeated nightmares about witches, for instance, or an unreasoning fear of dogs. A boy's phobia about a wild animal may be based on anxious rivalry with a father. Such an animal has the hugeness, strength, gruffness that the small boy feels threatened by in his father. Smokey, the fire-fighting bear, might be a particularly appropriate symbol of a just father because he also exhibits a stern disapproval of bad, destructive people. The frightening idea of forest fire could remind a child of both his own angry feelings, of which he feels so guilty, and the dangerousness of the imagined hostility of others.

There doesn't have to be any consistency or logic in the formation of a phobia, as long as different elements in it correspond to the emotions that have been repressed. The fact that Smokey was only intended to be a benign, cautionary figure is lost in the shuffle of the child's troubled feelings. I can still remember a phobia of fire engines I had in early childhood. Though I must have known that officially they help people by putting out fires, I actually felt as I heard one screaming through the night that it was a wild thing spreading fiery destruction.

☙ ☙ ☙

Freud, in treating people who were suffering from phobias and other neuroses, discovered how regularly some of the roots of their troubles could be traced back, through psychoanalysis, to this stage of childhood, with its love, rivalry, hostility, guilt, fear of genital injury ("castration anxiety"). He called it the "Oedipus complex" after the Greek myth of Oedipus who, through a series of tragic circumstances, was raised in ignorance of who his true parents were, killed his father in a fight and married his mother. When he learned the truth he blinded himself.

Some people who have heard of the Oedipus complex think it applies only to neurotic individuals. Others understand that Freud believed it plays a part in the development of everyone, but assume that its influence is always harmful to one degree or another. I think it is more correct to see this phase as a fundamentally constructive step in the development of normal human beings. Its painful aspects are like other ordinary tribulations of life: the hurts of accidents which teach caution; the early jealousy of brothers and sisters which is largely converted into altruism; the fights with friends in childhood which foster tolerance and co-operation; the early trials of couples which eventually strengthen their marriages.

The experience of falling in love with a good parent at this impressionable early age has a most profound effect, we have learned, in setting the romantic ideals of a child, and in preparing him to make a fine marriage and become a sound parent when the right time comes. Even the painful rivalry with the parent of the same sex enables the child eventually to gain more value from the relationship with that parent through the rest of childhood, and trains him not to fear but to handle in a constructive way the daily occupational rivalries with others of his sex the rest of his life.

DEALING WITH WORRIES AND
SEXUAL INTERESTS

It is wise to try to keep the anxieties
within reasonable bounds.

I HAVE BEEN describing some of the tensions that develop —
underneath the surface — in the age period between three and
six years. Now I'd like to discuss some of the practical aspects
of this stage of development.

First is the question of what should be done to help children
who develop nightmares or fear of the dark, or phobias about
animals or cripples, or other symptoms, in the three-to-six-year-
old period. Do they need professional help? It is impossible to
give an arbitrary answer. It depends on at least three more
questions: How severe is the symptom? How long is it lasting?
How is the child getting along in other respects?

A fair proportion of children develop occasional nightmares
or mild phobias at this age, which last for a few weeks or months
and then gradually disappear. If a child with a temporary symptom of this slight degree also has a good relationship with both
his parents, is not tied to their apron strings, is not too difficult

for them to manage, if he seeks the company of other children and is able to hold his own with them, then I think there would be no cause for the parent to worry or to try to get professional help.

On the other hand, if the nightmares occur regularly for months, or the child worries a lot about injuries or diseases or bogeymen or animals; if he is overdependent on one parent, or overawed by or defiant of the other parent; if he constantly handles his genitals (aside from the times when he has a full bladder) or is anxiously obsessed with getting other children undressed; if, as occasionally happens, a boy is so afraid of being a boy that he consistently pretends that he is a girl, or if a girl has such resentment of being her sex that she *always* insists on acting as if she were a boy, then the evidence is strong that the child is not coping adequately with the strains of this "Oedipal" period and needs some help from a child-guidance clinic or private psychiatrist. In communities where no child guidance is available there may be a family social agency to help the mother cope with the child's problem.

More important for most parents is to know how to guide their child through such a stage of development so that he doesn't get too mixed up.

⚡ ⚡ ⚡

What course should they take in regard to the occasional genital play which occurs in most normal, wholesome children around three and four years (in contrast to the constant handling of the anxious child)? At first the child may be so unaware of any possible disapproval that he makes no effort to hide it and even tells his parent that he does it because it feels good. I think the answer will vary somewhat, depending on the parents' beliefs. On the one hand are parents who are well aware of the medical view that no physical or emotional harm results from genital play itself in a well-adjusted child, who have no strong moral or religious objections to it, and who are not particularly bothered by it. They can matter-of-factly say something to the effect that this is not considered polite in public, just as urinating in public is not considered polite. A few parents might ask why it is necessary to go even this far. It perhaps would not be in one of the lands where childhood masturbation is not disapproved of by anyone. But in our country many people consider genital play in childhood wrong, and almost everybody objects to seeing it in public. This is why most child psychiatrists, I think, would advise parents to inhibit it this far. It doesn't help a child to bring him up thinking it's all right to offend the sensibilities of the community.

The same advice applies to sex play between different children, which is likely to be disapproved of by the majority of parents in any neighborhood and which will give a bad reputation to the child who persists in it.

Many parents whose religion definitely disapproves of genital play, or whose upbringing makes them distinctly uncomfortable when they see it in their children, despite what they have heard about medical opinion, will naturally want to discourage it, not only in public but in private too. (Lots of parents who thought they had got over any disapproval are quite surprised to find how anxiously they react when they unexpectedly find their child involved in it.) I think that parents who disapprove of or are bothered by genital play should discourage it — in a considerate way. They can't be good parents in other respects if they are uncomfortable with their children in one respect. Children always sense what their parents' feelings are. They prefer — most of the time — to be helped to conform. They aren't comfortable with parents who disapprove but who are trying to suppress their disapproval. The main things to avoid are giving the child the feeling that he (or she) will injure himself, or be injured, and giving him the feeling that this behavior is *much* worse than other kinds of misbehavior and might even make the parents reject him altogether.

Genital play can usually be discouraged, just the way other

disapproved behavior can be discouraged, by the parent's simply saying, "Mother doesn't want you to do it," or "It isn't polite," in a firm but trusting tone which implies, "I know that you'll do your best." When parents prohibit running into the street, it's usually done in a manner which clearly shows that it is the act which is disapproved. But sometimes when parents are disturbed by an act which has moral implications (stealing is another example), their anxiety may prompt them to land on the child with such a vigorous condemnation of *him* — as a person — that he doubts his own goodness and fears his parents will stop loving him altogether.

Another reason for not using threats of injury or of withdrawal of love for genital play is that we believe that even very obedient small children will yield to the temptation again on a few occasions (just as almost all adolescents do), which would then result in an increase in the sense of dread or unworthiness.

Circumcision is particularly inadvisable at this age, as you can imagine, because of the likelihood that the child will misinter-pret it.

¥ ¥ ¥

Another field for the practical application of our knowledge about the Oedipal stage of development is in answering young children's questions about the physical differences between boys and girls. To be realistic about it from the start, the evidence that we have suggests that it is not possible to explain the facts of life to a three-year-old in such a way that it prevents all worry about genital injury. But what is desirable is to keep the fear within reasonable bounds.

If parents realize how likely small children are to conclude that a girl was meant to have a penis and that a boy might easily lose his, they will be somewhat prepared to understand the meaning behind some of their children's questions, and to answer in a way that will be as reassuring as possible.

One trouble is that little children's questions so often pop out unexpectedly, not in the privacy of the home but in public. I've heard many stories about the discovery of sex differences at the beach. When a three-year-old girl points in amazement at the first boy she sees undressed and asks, "What's that?" or a boy says loudly, "Where's her wee-wee?" a polite mother's instinct is to say "Hush!" or "Don't point!" or to change the subject quickly. These responses aren't reassuring to a child who's just beginning to worry that there's skulduggery going on.

In the home it's less embarrassing. But most parents are surprised to see how they tense up when the first question comes, how they answer in an unfamiliar tone of voice, how they tend to give an evasive reply or pretend not to have heard.

When a new baby of the opposite sex comes home from the hospital, a child between two and six who has not seen nudity before is apt to ask questions the first time there is a diaper change or bath. If he is too startled to ask, the parent can usually see the concern written on his face.

There is occasionally the situation in which an only child is approaching five or six years of age and has presumably not seen other children or his parents undressed. I think this degree of innocence is actually much rarer than is usually assumed. There are few families which have so much space and privacy that a child sometime won't blunder into a bathroom or bedroom at a moment when a parent or other person is undressed, especially in these days of small homes and less modesty. Outside the home there are the unexpected glimpses in the neighbor's bathroom, at beaches, behind bushes in parks, in public toilets. There are the episodes when children deliberately undress, out of mutual curiosity, which are apt to happen occasionally unless they are constantly supervised. There are statues in museums and photographs of statues in books. On the farm and in zoos there are animals, and everywhere there are dogs.

But whether a small child has seen much or little, we should assume that his nature makes him curious and sensitive. We can be on the lookout for direct questions, for veiled questions, and for unspoken questions.

When the question comes, we need to explain, of course, that boys are made different from girls, and to give examples from among the child's friends and relatives. But psychiatrists have learned that when a child is upset by a question that's hard for him to face, it's not so effective to rush in with a hurried reassurance as it is to take a little time to get the worry out in the open first, so that the reassurance can hit the target. When the mother senses anxiety in her daughter's questions, she may be able to take time to explain: "That is the way a boy does wee-wee. It is called a penis. Sometimes when a girl sees that a boy has a penis, she wonders why she doesn't have one. She thinks she was meant to have one too. She thinks maybe she isn't made right or maybe she had a penis once but something happened to it. But that's not right. Girls aren't meant to have penises. All girls and ladies are meant to be made different from boys and men," and so on.

It's well to remember that such startling news as this cannot be understood in one sitting, nor will it remain understood for long at this stage of rapid psychological growth. If the child has grasped it at all, and if he has felt that his mother is willing to explain, he will mull it over and then reopen the question a day, a month, a year later. It's even more important then for the parent to listen attentively to his later questions to see where he is straight and where he is mixed up still.

A mother who has been too surprised by the first question to give a satisfactory answer needn't worry that the opportunity has been lost forever. If the child doesn't ask more in the next day or two, she can open up the subject again at a convenient time by saying, "I was thinking about that question you asked me the other day."

What about the child who asks no questions — at three or four or at five? We believe, from all professional experiences in the past quarter century, that there is no such thing as no awareness, no curiosity about such matters. We think that the child who has raised no questions has either become too anxious to ask, or has picked up some clue — from the parent's manner when he did try an earlier question — which told him this was a rather embarrassing subject. Then the parent needs to be a bit more attentive to the indirect questions: "Is a cow a mommy or a daddy?" "How does a doll go wee-wee?" My favorite example is a little girl who gazed thoughtfully at her plate and asked, "Is a frankfurter a boy or a girl?" Then there are all the actions which speak louder than words. A girl may be discovered trying to urinate standing up like a boy. Almost all little girls and boys, when they pick up a doll or a toy animal, instinctively turn it upside down for a quick glance at the genital area. Any such episode gives a mother the chance to observe, "I guess you have been wondering lately about why girls are made different from boys."

One other matter belongs in this discussion: the question of parental modesty or nudity. There has been a vigorous reaction in this century away from the extreme modesty and prudishness of the Victorian age. A great many parents today are fairly casual about letting their children in the room when they are dressing or bathing. Child psychiatrists have raised doubts whether the effect of this on children is as wholesome as was originally hoped. They have evidence that, in certain cases at least, a mother's nudity may be too exciting for her small son, the father's nudity too stimulating to his daughter. It accentuates the child's possessive wish for one parent and his rivalry with the other. Furthermore, in the case of the boy, the sight of his father undressed can exaggerate his enviousness and antagonism.

It's easy to see that the small child's relationship to his parents, which is so much more intense than to anyone else, makes their nudity a special situation.

I don't think we have enough knowledge today to say surely whether parental nudity is inadvisable in all families. The psychiatrists have secured their evidence from the study of children who have problems. Obviously a lot of children have grown up quite normal, as far as anyone can see, with parents who were more or less nudists at home. But this doesn't prove that the nudity was no strain at all on them. My own feeling is that, until we know more, it is sensible to advise parents to lean in the direction of reasonable modesty.

WHAT PART SHOULD
THE PARENTS PLAY?

*They can better cope with their children if they
understand the strains of unconscious rivalry.*

PARENTS WONDER whether children in the three-to-six-year-old
period, since they are subjected to special tensions, should be
managed with special consideration. I suppose the answer depends on what you mean by special consideration. I think
parents can better understand their children's behavior and are
in a better position to cope with it if they know something about
the strains that are likely to be experienced at this age. But there
is no way to ward off these strains altogether, and the attempt to
do so can create new difficulties.

Around the age of three and four years a boy's increasingly
romantic and possessive attachment to his mother makes him
gradually more aware that she already belongs to his father.
This arouses feelings of jealousy and antagonism. In his childish
way he assumes that his father knows all about his rivalrous feelings and reciprocates them. This is frightening, because his
father is so much bigger, and also because the boy admires him

greatly and is dependent on his love. (To imagine this predicament in adult terms, picture a man hopelessly in love with the wife of his best friend and boss who, he believes, has superhuman strength, is a mind reader, is very jealous, but in whose house he has to live.)

A little girl, because of her growing romantic attachment to her father, finds herself in a correspondingly uncomfortable rivalry with her admired mother.

Sometimes a conscientious father, who has heard that a little boy is apt to picture his old man as a stern, vengeful figure, resolves to lean over backward to be a genial playmate with his son and to avoid being the disciplinarian. A father is particularly likely to take this position if he remembers his relationship with his own father as having been strained. He wants his son to love and enjoy him more than he ever did his father. A mother may have the same kind of concern in rearing her daughter.

This aim sounds sensible enough at first glance. But child-guidance experience has shown that it usually does not work out as intended. One way of explaining it would be to say that a boy by his basic nature feels that his father *is* primarily a father and only secondarily a pal. All his experience tells him that his father is bigger, stronger, wiser than he. Therefore, he has to be in a dependent relationship to him — for protection and guidance. He realizes, too, that his father cares very much how he behaves, that he is pleased when he is co-operative or skillful or brave. He senses that his father is disappointed when he is timid or clumsy, irritated when he is rude, disobedient, or destructive, no matter how hard the father is trying to conceal these negative attitudes. To a degree, a boy's guilt, when he has misbehaved, demands some form of discipline. As for the rivalry, remember that it's the boy's own antagonism toward his father which is the main factor that makes him imagine that his father is antagonistic to him, no matter how thoroughly agreeable the father actually feels.

What this all adds up to is that a boy's very nature insists that his father is a somewhat awe-inspiring and slightly threatening figure.

Then what happens when a father is trying too hard to be only a friend? We have found, when the boy's unconscious attitudes are gradually revealed through months of child-guidance work, that such a father often seems more rather than less threatening than the average. Why should he seem more so?

When a father is hesitant to say what he expects, and always suppresses any irritation, this leaves the boy uncertain about his own behavior, and apprehensive about what the paternal anger would be like if it ever exploded. (Most of us imagine an unknown danger as worse than it turns out to be — whether it's the first trip to the dentist, childbirth, battle, or examinations.) We can put it another way by saying that since he senses that his father is occasionally holding back on his anger because he's afraid to let it go, the boy accepts the father's estimate that it is a very dangerous thing. (Perhaps you yourself were once subordinated to a teacher or boss who was suppressing his anger, and can remember how uneasy it made you.)

If a father is the usual self-confident kind who does not have doubts about whether his son loves him and who has no hesitation about being the leader — or even the disciplinarian when the occasion demands it — then the boy will be quite clear and comfortable about where he stands. The boy will have had occasional experiences of meeting his father's firmness and disapproval. He will find that he comes through these episodes safe and sound and a little bit wiser. This has a reassuring effect, just as it will be reassuring to him to find that he can ride a bike, keep afloat in swimming, hold his own with the other boys. The fact that his father isn't afraid of his own feelings teaches the boy not to be too afraid of them either. The fact that the air is cleared after a moment of firmness or disapproval or anger is a relief.

☙ ☙ ☙

There's another angle of the Oedipal situation that we ought to consider for a minute. The father who has heard about the rivalry that his son may feel toward him may think that it is fairer, more tactful if he himself refrains from claiming his wife's attention too obviously. Perhaps he keeps from showing much physical affection for her, or breaks off his conversation with her when the boy wants to talk to her, or is hesitant to butt in when he finds them together. He may avoid taking her out alone, except when the child is tucked in bed and asleep.

Experience shows that this degree of consideration for the child's feelings is apt to misfire. If he gets the impression that he has first rights to his mother, it only makes him more possessive, more jealous of his father's attentions to her. He'll be apprehensive of what he assumes *must* be his father's resentment. It eventually creates more difficulties for him when he is a little older and has to face realities.

A boy in the long run gets confidence in himself as a male, learns to enjoy rather than fear competition with other males, becomes appropriately bold with the opposite sex, not in beating out his father for his mother's attention but in patterning himself after his father, in feeling that he is a chip off the old block. So the old block must be impressive. The father needs to show himself — at home even more than outside — to be an agreeably self-confident male, reasonably masterful in protecting and providing for the family, comfortable in assuming his share of the discipline of the children, successful romantically with his wife. (Needless to say, the parents should not tease the child by being deliberately ostentatious with their mutual affection.)

＊＊＊

From what I have said about the relationship between father and young son, you'll be able to guess what I'll say about mother and daughter. In her unconscious mind a little girl feels that she is at the short end of an unfair rivalry. But it does not follow from this that a sensible mother should show her daughter extra consideration in the sense of being unnaturally patient and long-suffering in dealing with her day by day, or by minimizing the signs of her own affection for her husband.

I previously quoted from a letter in which a gentle mother expressed bewilderment at her four-year-old daughter's flashing-eyed defiance. She added that by contrast the girl was all peaches and cream with her father and was making a great show of taking care of him. When a child starts with a sense of having been treated a bit unfairly and then finds that the parent is willing to put up with rudeness or disobedience, it confirms the child's suspicion that the parent is guilty, and it unleashes further disagreeableness. The conscientious mother in the letter was assuming that, in some way which she didn't understand, she was failing her daughter. But in being willing to accept the blame and the unpleasant behavior, she was getting in deeper and deeper. (If I were she, I'd give my daughter a talking to about politeness and obedience and who's boss, and I'd check her firmly each time she forgot.) What keeps a little girl's unconscious rivalry within bounds is to find her mother a self-assured, unguilty, firm but friendly individual.

A mother does her daughter no favor in letting her gain the impression that she may be displacing her. (You sometimes see a girl in the full bloom of adolescence taking great delight in showing her affection for and understanding of her father when, because of menopausal or other troubles, there is a lot of grumpiness between her parents.) Such a short cut to success is apt to leave her a somewhat guilty, anxious, disagreeable person who may have trouble becoming detached from her father later. In the long run, a girl will gain more confidence in herself as an attractive girl, prepare herself for eventually falling in love with an appropriate man of her own age, by looking up to her mother as a fine example of romantic success, and identifying herself with her.

и и и

To round out this discussion, I'll add a few points about the father's relationship with daughter, mother's with son.

A daughter needs acceptance by and appreciation from her father, not only as a child but specifically as a girl. There are occasional cases in which a father was looking for a son, never got him, but instead treats his daughter as a son. He shows his enjoyment mainly when she is acting like a boy. We see how hard it is for such a girl as she grows up to get satisfaction from most of the jobs (including wifehood) that women have.

On the other hand, it doesn't help a little girl to grow up if her father lets her carry her romantic attentions to him as far as she wishes or if he responds to them with too much romantic enthusiasm of his own. It's good for his attitude toward her to have a flavor of chivalry and tenderness. But child-guidance work shows that if she is allowed to snuggle with him in a romantic mood, engage him in tickling games, climb into his bed, the effect is apt to be both stimulating and disturbing. And if he shows he has more fun passing the time of day with her than with his wife, then he is pulling her out of her orbit.

The corresponding points can be made about mother and young son. She lets him take the initiative in showing his manly devotion through helpful and chivalrous acts, and responds with gracious appreciation. She enjoys his rare compliments and admires the exploits that he tells her about. But when he carries his physical ardor beyond a hug, she tactfully distracts his attention. She doesn't dazzle him with deliberate displays of her lingerie or her nudity. She doesn't let him sleep in his father's bed when the latter is away on a trip, sensing that this will stir up hopes in his unconscious mind which will only backfire when his father comes home.

и и и

Perhaps at this point you have a feeling of impatience that I've used so many words to recommend a set of parental attitudes and procedures which are only what sensible parents have always used intuitively. It certainly is true that billions of parents since the beginnings of our race have brought their children up well without knowing about the Oedipus complex.

On the other hand, a certain proportion of children in each generation have been switched off the main track in passing through this phase, as history books, novels, and our knowledge of our friends show. And if everyone is to share in our newer knowledge about where the neuroses come from, I think he should be equally clear about what makes for successful character formation too.

Or perhaps you are impatient with Nature for using such a complicated pattern of development. Why is it necessary for little children first to get romantically attached to their parents, only to become so worried by the implications and so frustrated by the realities that they try to renounce the whole quest by the age of six or seven? We only know, from studies of different individuals who were either successful or unsuccessful in traversing this stage of development, that the romantic yearning for the parent — and the later renunciation — plays a vital role in the creation of some of the finest attributes of human nature: the spiritual quality of adult love and marriage, human idealism in general, religious belief, artistic creativeness, scientific curiosity, even the stability of society. That's quite a list and will take some explaining.

VI

Turning to the Outside World
After Six

PULLING BACK FROM
THE PARENTS

The noblest things that man has
thought and made are partly the
product of his longing for and then
renunciation of his beloved parent.

AFTER THE AGE of six or seven a child's interests and drives change surprisingly. He formerly spent most of his waking hours directly copying adult activities. A boy pushed toy cars around the floor, rode his tricycle as if he were a fireman, pretended his wagon was a trailer truck, built skyscrapers and bridges with blocks or boxes. When he got into dramatic family play he wanted to be the father and gave a pretty good imitation of his own father's behavior. A girl spent a good part of her time imitating the activities of her mother — right down to her tone of voice and the curl of her little finger when lifting a teacup.

From the age of six, a child of course spends most of his daylight hours in school. Have you ever stopped to wonder why this age was chosen, in most of the countries of the world where there are schools? It's not because children can't be taught many many things before six. The important difference is that they are now ready to understand impersonal, abstract symbols

— numbers and letters particularly. This requires a certain level of intelligence. It requires even more a positive interest in such impersonal things. To be sure, a younger child is interested in the number of his socks and in recognizing the letters that spell his name, but these are very concrete matters that have a personal significance to him. In the school years, numbers and letters and maps and diagrams become not only comprehensible but fascinating in themselves — just because they are abstractions.

There are many other matters not so unreal but still quite impersonal that become absorbing interests in the early school years: how machines work, how plants grow, how the earth was made.

Whom is the school-age child trying to pattern himself after? As far as you can see on the surface, the boy is much less interested in imitating his father. Instead, he is striving to be like the other kids in the neighborhood. I can still remember at seven no longer wanting the even-all-over haircut my father had always ordered for me. I wanted the regular-guy style of 1910: clippered right down to the white scalp all around, and a thick thatch on top, which we all tried to train into a "pompadour" by going to bed in skullcaps made from the tops of our mothers' black cotton stockings.

When a mother buys a new suit for a four-year-old, he's all eagerness to try it on. And when she beams on him, because he looks so cute in it, he beams too. He takes it for granted that her taste — in suits and in boys — is impeccable. But when a mother brings home a new suit for an eight-year-old he's more apt to scowl suspiciously before he's even seen it. He's so sure that boys' taste is the opposite from adults' taste that he half assumes the suit his mother has bought him will make a monkey of him with the gang.

He prefers old clothes (they are tried and true) and he prefers to wear them messy. He balks and argues against washing his hands, brushing his hair, taking a bath, as if these acts were painful or dishonorable.

Children in the preschool years make an earnest attempt to copy their parents' table manners. After six or seven they often look as if they are trying to see how much crudeness they can get away with. They sprawl over the table, guzzle their soup, and kick the leg of the chair.

Very young children strive to copy their parents' diction and vocabulary. They feel proud when they borrow big adult words whose meaning they don't yet understand. That's being grown up. In the school years they wouldn't be caught dead using precocious words. Now the aim is to pick up the words which their contemporaries use and which parents disapprove of, whether or not the meaning is exactly understood. Bad words are most relished. But if a child doesn't dare use these at home — even experimentally — he will ostentatiously and defiantly use the word "ain't" as if to say, "You can't keep me in innocence any longer. I'm finding out at last how they talk in the big rough world."

Play becomes increasingly impersonal too. No more playing house — no more playing mommy and daddy. The only kinds of people left in games are teams of cops and robbers or cowboys and Indians. What count now are skills, and rules, not the human drama. Most typical are games like rope skipping, hopscotch, jacks, mumble-the-peg, which are utterly impersonal.

Children are now apt to develop several irritating habits. These vary from child to child and from season to season: leaving doors open that are meant to be closed, slamming doors that should be closed gently, drumming on the table, dropping the coat always in the middle of the living-room floor, scratching the scalp, picking the nose, belching loudly and often without other evidence of indigestion. These drive parents mad; but no matter how frequently and firmly they correct the child, he always acts surprised or mistreated, as if he felt quite innocent. He is innocent as far as his conscious intentions are concerned, but I doubt whether anyone can be that irritating by accident.

A child in the school years will try to use the authority of adults outside the home — such as teachers — when he feels like arguing against his parents. "Miss Huckley says we don't need to wear snow pants until after Christmas." "Miss Huckley says the sky isn't really blue — it's black." A boy asks his doctor father, "Which are bigger, red blood cells or white blood cells?" The father falls into the trap of thinking he is being asked for information and is pleased. He says, "White blood cells are larger." The boy replies with a tone of voice in which belligerence is barely covered by politeness, "Oh no, they're not. Red blood cells are larger — our science teacher says so."

Some of these quotes from outside authorities are for the simple purpose of trying to gain privileges or to avoid having to be dressed differently from other children. But the topic and the tone of voice often show that the real purpose is to prove that the parents don't know all the answers. I don't think the child is as much interested in putting the parents in their place for their own good as he is in convincing *himself* that they aren't the final authority. He senses that if he is to continue to grow up and become an independent, co-operative citizen, he must learn to weigh the opinions of outsiders. To be free to do that he has first to outgrow his early-childhood idea that his parents are the wisest people in the world, the only ones whose knowledge needs to be considered at all.

🍂 🍂 🍂

What happens to the romantic attachments to parents? You can see most boys pulling back from their mothers after the age of six. They become less willing to be kissed and finally they balk altogether, at least in public. The thought of the mother in any romantic connection becomes objectionable. A father told me of a discussion in his family about what name to give a boat they were getting. He himself eventually suggested the endearing nickname by which he called his wife. The ten-year-old son promptly made a loud retching noise, as if he were about to vomit.

Some boys at six and seven continue to talk about their special girl friends of their own age. But a great majority, by nine or ten, protest loudly against the whole female sex. They call girls silly, disgusting. They groan when they have to see a preview glimpse of a love story in the movies. Of course they protest too much. Under the scorn there is obviously positive interest still, but it is certainly strongly repressed.

How do all these aspects of the six-to-twelve-year-old fit together? Freud found the meaning during his lifelong work in the psychoanalysis of patients, and it has been well confirmed by others. A boy's intense attachment to his mother in the three-, four-, five-year-old period is beset with difficulties. It creates feelings of rivalry with his beloved father, which he assumes his father reciprocates, and this frightens him. At the same age he misinterprets the meaning of the physical difference between boys and girls and fears that he might lose his own penis, perhaps as punishment for sex play or for his wish to supplant his father. He represses these anxieties into his unconscious mind. But they eventually get so disturbing that the romantic feelings for his mother lose their positive, pleasant aspect and become uncomfortable; he wants to avoid them and forget them.

This turning of positive feelings into negative feelings, because of painful associations, takes place in other situations and age periods too. You may remember some food that you previously loved and then became disgusted with, because you became ill once soon after eating it.

Of course a boy continues to love his mother deeply as comforter, protector, guide. He just senses that he has to give up the special yearning for her that implies competition with his father.

Freud called this renunciation (around the age of six) the resolution of the Oedipus complex. He named the stage from then until the beginning of adolescence the latency period, in the sense that the romantic and sexual drives, which played such a vital part in the child's emotional growth between the ages of three and six, are, for the time being, largely repressed.

But the slowing down of one aspect of development is the very means of fostering others. There is lots of evidence that the child's renunciation of his intense, personal devotion to his parent frees his mind for academic learning. It makes all the subjects that are studied in school particularly welcome just because they are impersonal.

But the readiness for academic learning is only part of the story. The transformation of interests — in the latency period and afterward — is not so fundamental or complete as it seems on the surface. The psychoanalyst, when he studies the dreams and thought associations of a patient, often finds connections in the unconscious mind between curiosity about science, for instance, and curiosity about the mysteries of sex and reproduction. Similarly he finds that the drive to create new inventions, works of art, and literature may be partly derived from the yearning to create children. As a matter of fact, the world has always said that the creative individual "gives birth" to his idea or project. So we can say that the noblest things that man has thought and made are partly the product of his longing for and the renunciation of his beloved parent.

The same can be said of the spiritual, idealistic, and chivalrous aspects of human love. If there were no Oedipal period, followed by the inhibitions of latency, love in the sexual sense would consist of a succession of brief physical attractions, such as occur in many animals, which involve no particular tenderness, no devotion, no establishment of family. The fact that a boy's first intense love is for his mother, who is vitally important to him in so many respects, that it occurs in the stable setting of the devoted family, that it imitates the admired father's love of the mother, all these attributes of the first love are what impel the boy, when he is grown, to channel his love in a similar pattern. But if he remained throughout the rest of life as in love with his mother as he was at the ages of three and four, he'd never be able to take another girl very seriously. (In real life we see an occasional man who can never love any woman but his mother and an occasional girl who never finds anyone as good as daddy.) So if the child is to grow up whole, there first must be the romantic love for the parent, and then it must be suppressed.

I have been talking almost exclusively about the boy and the vicissitudes of his relationship with his mother. But the resolution of the Oedipus complex brings a shift in his relationship with his father too. Before, his feelings were a mixture of almost slavish admiration and considerable unconscious fear. Now, on the surface, it looks very much as though he were pulling away from his father, as from his mother, giving him up as a model, arguing with him.

But when we look more deeply into his feelings we find that he had succeeded so well in identifying with his father that he now feels like a grown-up, independent man-of-the-world in his own right. He doesn't have such an intense need any longer to look constantly to his father for his cues.

This transformation recalls the old saying, "If you can't lick him, join him." From now on he is in a position to continue to learn from his father in a more selective, man-to-man way, and at the same time to learn much more about the outside world as a replica of his father.

A girl comes to the resolution of her Oedipus complex, too, in repressing her wish to have her father for herself, in order to lessen the uncomfortable rivalry with her mother. She makes a more thorough identification with her mother and turns her interest to the less personal outside world. But on the average the shift is less drastic and less complete in the girl. She usually doesn't have to be quite as balky and messy as her brother; she's apt to find less fascination than he in mathematics, mechanics, and science. In other words, she isn't compelled to repress so vigorously her personal feelings, and this shows up quite clearly in her ability still to express affection for her father and to accept it from him.

ACQUIRING A
STRICT CONSCIENCE

Underneath the surface you can

see subtle signs of a

new kind of self-discipline.

INEXPERIENCED PARENTS are apt to think their first child is going to the dogs sometimes in the six-to-twelve-year-old age period. He seems to have lost most of his table manners. He balks at hair brushing, hand washing, baths. He's more likely than not to keep his room and possessions in an awful mess. His language may be rough or worse. He's often argumentative and sometimes quite rude. He is apt to develop irritating habits that grate on his parents' nerves; they beg him or command him to stop these, but he always forgets.

This is the surface picture. But if you have the patience to look underneath the surface you can see subtle signs of a new kind of self-discipline. Psychologists have made careful observations of what seven-year-olds talk about, during recess periods, for instance, and find that a surprising amount of time is spent discussing what's proper behavior — not from an adult's viewpoint, of course, but from their own. They criticize classmates whom they consider out of line in any direction.

I think that this concern about behavior is one of the reasons why children keep forming secret societies at this age. Several boys, who play together anyway because they have a common point of view, suddenly decide to formalize their solidarity with all the trappings of a dignified men's club — name, bylaws, officers, badges. It helps each one to feel surer that he is a right-thinking individual if he is publicly associated with a right-thinking group. The group can further convince themselves that they have the correct standards by ostentatiously excluding those who differ from them.

The club idea helps them in another way. The secrecy is a legitimate excuse for keeping parents and teachers at a distance. For how can you feel you are establishing your own code of behavior when adults are constantly telling you what to do — as if you were too young to know?

The games that become increasingly fascinating, like hop-scotch, jacks, mumble-the-peg, show how strong the drive for self-discipline is. Part of the appeal is the development of skill for its own sake. If you had never seen such games but had only heard somebody describe how hard children practice them, hour after hour and day after day, you might assume that stern grownups were driving them to these tasks. Actually, parents have to pull their children away from such games by the scruff of the neck for meals, and teachers have to keep a sharp watch to prevent jacks contests from springing up in the corridors of school.

Even the messiest child between six and twelve will have moments of orderliness. Suddenly he feels the urge to systema-tize his comic books. He gathers the dusty things from every corner. He sits happily among them for hours, stacking them by title and date. Or he decides to organize all the stuff in his desk drawers. The psychological closeness between messiness and orderliness shows up in the glee with which he first dumps the contents of all the drawers in a huge pile in the middle of the floor. Sometimes he collects such a mountain of possessions that his enthusiasm runs out before he gets very far in organizing them. His mother in desperation has to finish the job.

Formal collections blossom now, too: stamps, rocks, trading cards. The chief delight is in trying to complete the collection, and to arrange it according to some system. Those girls who, after seven or eight years, are still interested in dolls are apt to take less pleasure in mothering them or having them act family roles. Instead, dolls, paper dolls, and their clothes become more like collections.

🚩 🚩 🚩

An aspect of the growing strictness of the child, which may irritate his father, is the way he watches the speed limit signs and the car's speedometer. He has no hesitation in telling his father, "You are going thirty-eight miles an hour and the speed limit is thirty-five." A parent feels that since he has taught the child right and wrong, the child should take it for granted that the parent is doing right, whatever he does. That was true earlier, but not after seven or eight. The child is now looking to the outside world for the rules and is unconsciously trying to outgrow his previous deference to his father as the ultimate authority. Under these circumstances it gives him considerable satisfaction to discover that this man, formerly presumed to have godlike righteousness, is actually a lawbreaker. From the point of view of the child's own increasing self-discipline, the significant thing about this attention to the speed limits is the literal-mindedness with which he takes the rules. To put it in different words: this is the age when an individual's conscience is at its most strict and most arbitrary. There are no grays — only blacks and whites.

Another sign of the severity of conscience now is the frequency of what psychiatrists call compulsions. They are somewhat like superstitions, but more bothersome and more private. One that many children share, around eight, nine, and ten years of age, is stepping over cracks in the sidewalk. They find themselves doing this even if they have never seen anyone else doing it. In the dim past, long before there were psychiatrists or psychoanalysts, children sensed vaguely the meaning of such a habit and said a joking rhyme about it: "Step on a crack, break your mother's back." This is a way of saying: "When my mother is cross to me and the thought flashes through my mind 'I wish she'd slip on a banana peel,' I feel so guilty that I have to step over a crack to undo the evil wish." This is so different from the attitude of a four-year-old, who doesn't feel conscience-stricken at all when he points a pretend pistol at his mother and says gleefully, "Bang! I'm shooting you dead."

The emergence of the child's own conscience and its relationship to his striving to be more independent of his parents show up in his new attitude toward religion, if he is growing up in a religious family. Back when he was four or five he saw that his father looked up to God the way he himself looked up to his father. You might say he felt he was related to God through his father (somewhat the way he's related to his grandfather) and accepted God on his parents' terms. But when he begins to pull back from his parents, questions their rightness (at least in surface matters), and looks to the outside world for his cues about what authority to look up to, it is quite natural that God will — to a degree — replace his father as the ultimate authority. And his inner need to define sharply between right and wrong makes him not only willing but glad to accept the church's doctrines. I don't mean to say that children at this age have much sense of communicating with God in an intimate, personal way — that comes later — but that they now give allegiance to Him in their own right.

☙ ☙ ☙

What is the over-all meaning of this system-loving, rule-making, self-disciplining, conscience-strengthening aspect of development, in the six-to-twelve-year-old period? In previous chapters, I discussed the emotional development of the child in the earlier phase between three and six, how he grows in wisdom and character through his very intense attachment to each of his parents, forming through their example his ideals of manhood and womanhood. But such ties must eventually be loosened if a child is to go on to make a good adjustment to the outside world. This is brought about primarily by the increasing sense of rivalry which he feels toward the parent of the same sex. The dangers which he imagines in this rivalry make him eventually give up the fantasy that he can somehow have the other parent for himself. He largely suppresses his romantic and sexual interests. He turns with some relief to the less personal outside world and becomes fascinated with abstract matter such as arithmetic, reading, mechanics, nature.

If a boy can't beat his father, he can join him, and a girl can join her mother. He no longer has to try so hard to be like his father because, inside, he's more convinced that he already is an independent man-of-the-world just like his father. Because of his touchy pride in his independence, he doesn't want to accept his rules from his parents. But having been brought up with a sense of right and wrong and a desire to be accepted, he must fill the vacuum with rules from somewhere and he looks to his pals, his teachers, his religion. His uneasiness about being newly on his own, morally speaking, makes him almost slavishly responsive to his own unsophisticated conscience. The reason his parents don't see this conscientiousness is that he is showing them so much rebelliousness in regard to superficial matters like cleanliness, manners, and chores.

In a most serious sense the child between six and twelve is working strenuously to prepare himself for adaptation to the outside world — to learn its skills, to obey its laws, to co-operate with its citizens. His job is made doubly difficult by the fact that at the same time he has to emancipate himself actively to some degree from his parents. This is painful to them and to him because he's nowhere near mature enough to do it graciously. He has to do it by differing, by arguing, by irritating. This happens whether or not his parents are trying to keep him too dependent. In other words, it's his own dependence which he's primarily fighting against.

THE CONTINUING NEED FOR
PARENTAL CONTROL

*You stick to the rules
you consider essential.*

❦❦❦❦❦❦❦❦❦❦❦❦❦❦❦❦❦❦❦❦❦❦❦❦❦❦❦❦❦❦❦

HOW ARE PARENTS to cope with the peskiness of the school-age child? Just to be understanding and patient isn't enough — it doesn't improve his behavior or spirits. To give him a free hand to be as difficult as he likes isn't good for him and it's intolerable for the parents. As I'm sure you know, there's no neat solution.

In the two preceding chapters, I've described some of the characteristics of the six-to-twelve-year-old. He is trying to accomplish at least three major changes — all at the same time:

1 — He wants very earnestly to fit into the world outside his home, and to imitate the other kids of his own age and sex;

2 — He wants to become more independent of his parents;

3 — His nature insists that he devote a lot of energy to learning skills, systematizing things, respecting laws, and strengthening his conscience.

These aims when listed in these words don't sound too difficult for parents to deal with. But in actuality — especially in the case of a boy — they can turn out to be quite annoying. The things which he chooses particularly to imitate in other boys, and with which he declares his independence of parents, are apt to be sloppiness in dress, reluctance to bathe and wash, crude table manners, vulgarity in language, argumentativeness, sometimes rudeness. His devotion to the learning of skills is not too impressive at home because it consists of such matters as making stinks or explosions with chemicals, or whirling whirly-whirlers. Most of his learning of skills goes on at school and he won't talk about that at home. His joy in systematizing is applied to collections of comics or bugs rather than to keeping bureau and desk drawers in order. The rules of conduct which he picks up eagerly in the outside world, and sometimes quotes disapprovingly against his parents, he often forgets to follow himself. His conscientiousness shows more often in stepping over cracks than in performing his chores.

The frequency with which children of this age manage to be irritating makes you wonder whether they could be doing it on purpose. Special psychological tests that were once given to a group of seven-year-olds revealed that they felt, deep down, that their parents were oppressing them constantly and that life was grim. Since these were the same parents whom they had looked up to and enjoyed when they were three and four, we have to assume that it was the children who had changed. What this means, I believe, is that their determination to be less dependent on their parents makes them feel antagonistic toward them. But they can't admit this, so instead they picture their parents as being domineering and antagonistic toward them. You can see signs of somewhat the same pattern in the automatic contrariness toward the parent of the one-year-old when he first senses that he's a separate person, as if he were always looking for an argument. You can see it in a much more complex way in the touchiness of many children around fifteen years of age, who complain, in answering questionnaires, that their parents don't understand them or treat them fairly, whereas younger and older teen-agers don't feel nearly so strongly about this.

So I think that the six-to-twelve-year-old is really trying to be irritating sometimes, though he doesn't realize this consciously. It's no wonder, then, that the parents, who were accustomed to so much admiration from him at an earlier age, now frequently find him standoffish, unpleasing, pesky.

Are there any solutions? I do think myself that it's some consolation for the inexperienced parent to learn that the grittiness which comes between him and his school-aged child is not a sign that the parent has lost his touch or that his child is in trouble. If he can think of these new behavior trends as proofs that the child is making progress in the long, hard business of growing up, then the parent, though he may still not enjoy the behavior, can at least smile wryly and knowingly, at his spouse or to himself. He will get less tense on certain occasions and this will prevent a number of blowups, to the benefit of the whole family.

How are the father and mother to manage the child, from hour to hour and day to day? Parents who have tried to be excessively understanding and patient have usually found that this is no answer. When a child, like an adult, finds that there is no one willing to set limits for his conduct, it makes him uneasy inside. He senses that he needs controlling. He's apt to react by trying to provoke those around him to crack down. He behaves more and more irritatingly, as if to say, "How bad do I have to get before you'll stop me?" He forces the parents to lose their temper eventually. But if they are the kind who believe they should remain sweetly agreeable under all circumstances, they'll feel a wave of remorse soon after the blowup. Then, in one way or another, they're inclined to turn apologetic. This undoes the correction and gives the child permission to act up again.

There is every reason to believe that a child of this age, with his strong inner sense of right and wrong, needs to be kept from meanness, destructiveness, rudeness, deliberate disobedience, just as much as a child of any other age. He also needs to feel the obligation to perform his routine chores, to lend a hand at

other times when requested, to come home for meals on time.
Furthermore, his parents must — for their own sake as well as
his — make him comply with minimal standards in table manners, politeness to company, personal cleanliness. If they don't,
they won't be able to stand him, and then they'll be more irritable with him in the end.

☙ ☙ ☙

From what I've said, so far, it doesn't sound as if any allowances should be made for his age and nature. There is still room
for special consideration, though. What he resents most is being
talked down to in a chiding tone of voice. Inside, he is longing
to be a dignified man-of-the-world. He thinks he is well along
the way. If his mother corrects him in a tone of voice which
implies that he knows nothing about proper behavior and is just
a small bad boy, this shatters his illusion and grates on him.

Yet even when he has the best of intentions he *does* have to
be jacked up, and quite often, as you know. So your first step,
I think, is to have a few rules which you yourself consider essential, such as a bath every night but Friday, his bike in the garage
for the night, no absent-minded kicking of the dining-room-table
leg, bed at 8:30.

You have to stick to your rules through thick and thin. When
the child is slightly overdue or out of line, the trick is to ask him
to do what you want, firmly but cordially, as if you were speaking to a respected friend who had asked to be reminded. He'll
wait another minute, to see whether your attention will wander,
but don't let it.

Of course the unrealistic factor in this advice about friendly
firmness is that a mother can't help getting cranky after hours
of needling from her child, whether the needling is gentle or
fiendish. The only defense I know is for the mother to remind
herself, at least once a day, that some of the child's behavior *is*
simply needling. If she can see this as a kind of fencing match in

which the child feels obligated to take the initiative, then, instead of feeling bewildered or hurt or outraged each time she gets pricked, she can take a certain pride in her shrewdness in anticipating and parrying his attacks, so that she can get her way in the end.

When I suggested that you stick to a few rules which you consider essential, I meant you might try to discard, for the time being, the less essential ones. These will of course differ a great deal from family to family. When our own children were this age, my wife and I resolved, for instance, to ignore chronically untied shoelaces (which were the symbols of independence of one of them), disheveled clothes (except on special occasions), unbrushed hair (except at the beginning of the day). We dropped the routine requirement of hand washing before meals unless the hands were so dirty they'd take our appetite away. On the other hand, I remained firm (masterfully firm when I could manage it) about fingernails being fairly clean, knowing that I couldn't be civil for very long to a child with black ones.

An understanding parent takes into account the child's strong wish to dress like, get haircuts like the other children in the neighborhood, even though these styles may not appeal to the parent very much. Of course I don't mean that the parent should feel bound to agree to what is quite unsuitable. It's also considerate to let the child have generally the same kinds of possessions that most of the other nearby children have — provided that these things are sensible and within the family's means. It's not that a child should feel that he can demand and get whatever he says all the other kids have. (There's a good chance he's exaggerating.) On different occasions it might be appropriate for him to buy what he craves from his allowance, or take on a special job to earn the extra money, or wait for his birthday. I'm only making the point that those parents who, for instance, are extracritical of the trashiness of ordinary comic books or the toy of the moment should take into account the child's craving to be in the swim, before letting their own taste decide.

The suggestions I've made so far haven't been very constructive ones. I've been talking as if the school-aged child were always on the offensive in asserting his independence and as if the best the parent could do was to find tricky ways to avoid getting frustrated and bruised. But the parents can give a child a little assistance in his own instinctive drive to become a more responsible citizen, if they are very tactful. It's a matter of assigning jobs, or letting the child take on jobs (such as a paper route), which are just difficult enough to be challenging, but which do not require so much maturity that he is bound to fail or has to be nagged endlessly. The inexperienced parent can get advice about suitability of jobs from other parents who have been through the mill, or from the schoolteacher. This is a good topic for a P.T.A. discussion. Also I'd advise you not to expect a majority of kids to be faithful to a job that lasts a long time or keeps repeating (like snow shoveling), unless there is an adult with leadership qualities in fairly close supervision.

In general, I think that the parents do not have as much opportunity now to refine the child's behavior and mold his interests — directly, positively, and in detail — as they did earlier when he was eager to adopt their patterns. So, in a sense, their job is mainly a holding operation, to keep him from backsliding. They have to count on him to do a good part of the work on his further maturation. He will be utilizing both the ideals he learned earlier from them and the experiences he is having in the neighborhood, in school and in other groups.

VII

The Strains of Adolescence

THE TEEN–AGER'S NEED
FOR GUIDANCE

Adolescents not only still need
guidance but actually want it.

QUITE A FEW years ago a mother and her fifteen-year-old daughter were in the waiting room of my office. I hadn't known them before and I didn't know what the problem was going to be either. After we introduced ourselves I asked the girl to côme in first.

Any boy or girl at this stage of life is very conscious of growing up, anxious to be considered a person in his own right, impatient of being thought of as only somebody's child. He appreciates being recognized as the main person when going to the doctor, going shopping, or having an interview with a college admission officer. If the visit has anything to do with conflicts between child and parent, a teen-ager feels more grumpy if his parent is interviewed first. He's apt to jump to the conclusion that the parent is putting most of the criticism on him and that the professional person will accept the parent's view of the situation hook, line, and sinker. After all, adults usually do *seem* to stick together and take each other's word when it comes to children.

I asked the girl what the problem was. She said that her parents wouldn't let her have the independence that other girls of her age have. Her particular complaint was that they wouldn't let her go to the football games with her classmates or attend the Friday night dances at the high school. We talked for a while about school, friends, hobbies, and home life, and then I said I'd like to talk with her mother, also alone.

When I asked the mother what the problem was, she said that she and her husband had become alarmed by the fact that the girl was gradually drawing into a shell and making all sorts of excuses for not being with her friends. The mother used as specific examples her daughter's refusal any longer to attend the football games and dances, despite the parents' cajoling, urging, and even secretly arranging invitations from other classmates.

I couldn't believe my ears at first. I knew well enough that in family conflicts different members often make the same situation sound surprisingly different. But I had never heard the main problem expressed in such diametrically opposite terms. It so happened that within a couple of months I talked with another family in which the adolescent daughter complained bitterly that her parents wouldn't let her do the very thing that the parents told me they were trying to get her to do. Then I realized that I hadn't been dreaming the first time and that there was something of general significance about adolescents here.

I don't mean that these girls were average or that there was no serious problem. When an adolescent (or a person of any age, for that matter) begins to avoid his old friends and activities, it means that he is under a great deal of inner tension and should have psychiatric help.

But these aggravated cases made me aware of how often, in more ordinary family situations, the adolescent complains indignantly that he isn't being allowed enough freedom or enough privileges, when a careful, unbiased investigation will show that he isn't being held back by his parents nearly as much as he feels he is. To be sure, parents have to be parents even to their teen-agers. They still have to set reasonable limits, not to be mean but because they love their children, know their inexperience, want to protect them from harm and from neighborhood criticism. And all good adolescents protest occasionally against limitations, even those that they know, underneath, are reasonable. Then, too, parents — being human — err in their judgment at times, being in one situation stricter than is really necessary or is customary in that neighborhood (which gives the child an excuse to be resentful), in another situation being more lenient than is sensible (giving the child a precedent to argue with on future occasions).

☙ ☙ ☙

But making full allowances for the frailties of human nature — in parents and in adolescents — still doesn't explain why a teen-ager gets so unjustifiably mad on occasions. There are two special reasons that I'm thinking of: first, his own dependence on his parents; and second, his uncertainty about his ability to carry off a grown-up role.

We are accustomed to think of younger children as dependent on their parents, running to them when hurt or in trouble or needing any kind of help, accepting their standards and rules about important matters, arguing only about minor regulations such as bedtime and what to wear. We think of adolescents, on the other hand, as always insisting on their independence. Gradually we as parents let ourselves be convinced by them that they are ready for it and entitled to it. It's because they are so one-sided in their arguments with us that we forget that actually, underneath, they are very much of two minds about their readiness for freedom. In fact, it sometimes seems as if their very nearness to independence frightens them into spells of dependence such as an eight- or ten-year-old would not experience.

Of course the teen-agers themselves never admit their desire for dependence at times, either to their parents or to themselves. But they show their need for it indirectly. I think of a sixteen-year-old boy who was constantly declaring that he was old enough to take care of himself completely but who felt indignant and hurt if his mother didn't occasionally have his sandwich, milk, and dessert all laid out on the table when he came home for lunch. Another takes it for granted that his parents will have anticipated his need for the car on a certain evening, though he forgets to mention it ahead of time. A girl may be hurt that her mother isn't able to drop all other plans in order to do an emergency job on her clothes for a date. Such things happen even though the adolescent is usually a co-operative and self-reliant person. What on the surface seems like a whole-hearted claim for independence is really a stormy vacillation between that claim and a longing to be cared for like a small child still.

The adolescent's inner doubts about his capacity to play a grown-up part in the world are not hard to understand if we stop to think or, better still, remember back to our own youth. First of all, adolescents want desperately to make the right impression. They've lost that casual ability to take themselves for granted which makes younger children relatively unself-conscious. It will be years before they reach the blessed adult stage of not worrying too much, most of the time, about what the world thinks of them (if it thinks at all).

They want to possess *all* the characteristics that seem ideal at this stage: attractiveness, knowledgeability, sophistication, skillfulness in a variety of activities. They haven't yet realized, as most of us adults have, that there is room in this world for dozens of different kinds of people and that each of us manages to get along and to find friends, despite a variety of imperfections.

They have so recently become aware of their intense ideals

that they have had too little time in which to practice them. They have to try to seem very knowledgeable with quite incomplete knowledge. Their feelings are too new and impulsive to be handled with sophistication. Their bodies are too hurriedly grown to be always managed gracefully and their skin is troublesome when they most want it perfect. The intensification of sexual awareness comes so suddenly and so strongly that it's hard to fit into the total scheme of life. As a result, it is a source of distress as often as it is exhilarating. How do you attract the appealing ones of the opposite sex and what do you do when they become interested? It's easy enough to daydream about coping suavely with these situations, but when they actually come up they create turmoil. To a shy child in early adolescence, the question of whether to try (or permit) hand-holding can be an overwhelming preoccupation all evening long, and how to fill in with conversation is even more baffling.

🖋 🖋 🖋

I have been emphasizing the worrisome side of the adolescent's nature, which is only half the picture. Some lucky children, as you know, seem to be able to breeze through the whole period with only minor storms. (As you can imagine, I made hard going of it myself.)

I have focused on the teen-ager's anxiety that he won't be able to carry off his role as man-of-the-world and on his hidden desire at times to still be taken care of by his parents because together they help to explain his unjustified reproaches that his parents don't give him enough freedom. *At these moments it's the adolescent himself or herself who is scared of freedom or some aspect of it* (like the shy girl who's afraid of the dances). But he certainly couldn't admit it to anybody, least of all to himself. That would be a betrayal of everything he stands for. Unconsciously, though, he can't escape some feeling of shame about his timidity and inadequacy. It makes him mad. He feels like lashing out at somebody. Who's trying to keep him tied to his parents' apron strings? he asks himself. Why, it must be the parents, of course. To prove the point conclusively, he may make some particularly unreasonable request, and when they refuse, he reproaches them with all the indignation he can muster.

What's the answer? It's helpful to parents if they know that some of these unjustified reproaches are a form of overprotesting. Then the parents can stick to their guns about what's sensible, without having to search their souls each time as to whether they are being fair. And it's good for parents to know that adolescents not only still need reasonable guidance but actually want it. Even though they don't admit this to their parents, they admit it sometimes to trusted teachers in school or psychiatrists in clinics. I've heard girls say, "I wish my mother would make rules for me like my friends' mothers do." They sense that they are still immature. They sense that standards give a dignity to life and that rules make life more comfortable to live. They even sense that reasonable parental control is one aspect of parental love and feel neglected when it's absent.

TEEN–AGE
IDOLS

No need for
parents to despair.

THERE ARE a variety of ways in which teen-agers bother their parents. The one that I'm thinking of here is the infatuation that millions of girls declare for one singer or movie actor or another. Some parents of each decade think that this is a new affliction and wonder what has come over the younger generation. But this kind of mass adoration has been taking place off and on for many years. I suppose that in earlier generations — before TV, radio, movies, and phonograph records — conditions did not favor such nationwide epidemics. In cities, though, certain matinee idols of the stage drew the same kind of frantic enthusiasm.

Adults read with amazement about long lines of adolescents waiting for hours outside the theater before the star appears, then greeting every step of his performance with tumultuous applause. They become uneasy when they hear of girls shrieking and sobbing and swooning. If they see a performance themselves on TV or film, they may, in certain cases, be disgusted. City officials and other groups have got so mad and alarmed that they have even tried to keep a performer from coming to town.

There are a number of aspects of adolescence that help to explain this phenomenon. I want to talk first about emotional and sexual development in general — and particularly in boys, because I remember it so well. I'll come back to girls later.

🎵 🎵 🎵

In the three-to-five-year-old period, boys and girls go through a stage of emotional development in which there is considerable interest in romance and sex, at a childish level. They love to play at being father and mother and taking care of their pretend children. Boys develop a particularly intense romantic attachment to their mothers and often speak of marrying them. Normal girls feel the same way about their fathers. Boys and girls are apt to become involved in sex play with each other and with themselves.

We've learned from psychiatric work that children become somewhat anxious and guilty about their sexual interests by the time they are five or six years old, partly because of parental disapproval, partly because of rivalry with the parents and partly because of misunderstandings about the physical differences between boys and girls. It's a complex matter which I've discussed more fully in the section "Attachments and Anxieties Between Three and Six." Children come to think of sex as bad and dangerous, to some degree, and they make vigorous efforts to suppress their interest in it. This period of intense repression lasts from about the age of six to the beginning of puberty development, which comes at eleven years for the average girl and thirteen for the average boy. The repression is so successful that, by the age of nine or ten years, most boys declare loudly that girls are silly, irritating, and repulsive. Girls retaliate by agreeing that boys are impossibly rough and mean, which they often are. (Of course the persistence with which the sexes scorn each other and tease each other at this age shows that they still retain considerable interest in each other, underneath.)

The glandular changes of puberty which bring about a rather violent reawakening of personal and sexual feelings have to work against these deeply ingrained habits of repression. As a result, the child often does not recognize the feelings for what they are at first and he continues to try to ignore them for some time afterward. We have come to realize, through psychoanalysis, that he partially understands them in his unconscious mind, yet largely fails to understand them consciously. What conscious knowledge he does have is kept vague and confused by the tension in his feelings, compounded as they are of excitement, inhibition, and guiltiness. Altogether, sex is more uncomfortable than pleasurable in the early stages of adolescence.

There are a number of different attitudes that will eventually blend together to create a mature romantic love: companionableness, protectiveness, joy in planning the future together, as well as sexual attraction. But in the young adolescent they are not ripening at the same rate and they don't mix smoothly. So his friendliness may go out to one girl, his chivalry to another, and his sexual interest to a third.

Many boys have acquired such a strong conviction that sex is bad that they are unable to feel any sexual interest at first toward the "nice" girls for whom they feel respect or tenderness. They can only respond in this way to girls who seem "bad." This division of love into two compartments, and the division of the opposite sex into two categories, occurs to varying degrees in many girls at first too. (In a few individuals of both sexes it persists into adulthood and of course makes for serious marital problems.)

The adolescent slowly gains sexual maturity by becoming

more accustomed to his new self, step by step, and also by becoming romantically interested in a succession of girls. Through them he learns not only about girls, but about himself.

As a matter of fact, the boy's most intense feelings of admiration may go out, in the very first stage of puberty, not to a girl — who is still taboo — but to a male teacher, or coach, or hero. Many girls have crushes on revered women at this stage too. When a boy does get up the courage to think romantically about girls, he may find it much safer to daydream about an adventure with a faraway movie actress than with a home-town girl whom he might run into an hour later. Even after he realizes that he is interested in a girl nearby, he may be quite content for months merely to think about her and make no move to speak to her or show his feelings.

His first love may be a choice which baffles his family and friends. They can detect no visible common interest on which it could be based. As time goes on, his preferences are apt to become more realistic and longer lasting. But it's only after a number of years that he is ready to recognize the girl who will be right for him for life and is able to offer her the combination of mature attitudes in himself that will make him right for her.

Perhaps you think I'm laying it on too thick, in the picture I've been drawing of bashfulness and bewilderment. There are some boys and girls who — even from the very beginning of adolescence — approach the opposite sex with apparent suavity. (In fact, there are a few children, brought up delinquently, who never develop any sexual inhibitions even in the six-to-twelve-year-old period.) I suspect, though, that the sophisticated early adolescents are good actors who are really less sure of themselves than they seem. But as they succeed with their bluffing they gain real confidence quickly. The timid ones aren't able to take advantage of the opportunities that would teach them more assurance.

Even if I have been giving a lopsided picture by emphasizing the more inhibited type of early adolescent, the points that I have been making are true of every normal teen-ager to a degree.

☙ ☙ ☙

Now we can get back to the response of girls in their early teens to the love songs and other seductive approaches of the singers and actors of the moment. Of course different personalities appeal to different girls. There is also the element of fashion, which makes one type particularly acceptable for a few years, and then another — just like clothes. There are various idols — the strong silent man, the wholesome boy, the tough guy, the wistful boy who seems to need mothering, the sexy male. Whatever type, they all have the advantage that they can be dreamed about, to the heart's content, without ever having to be coped with. A girl in her imagination can have the idol say or do anything she wants, and she herself can be irresistible. No risk of being spurned because she is unattractive or of being tongue-tied or of having the actor prove hard to manage. (During a trip abroad in 1924 on a college athletic team, my friends and I managed to get ourselves introduced to Gloria Swanson, the reigning movie queen. But in an agonizing full circuit of the dance floor on the ocean liner I couldn't find one single word to say to her, even though she graciously tried to help me.)

What parents find particularly hard to take is the sexual suggestiveness of an occasional performer who has no appeal to them at all, and — harder still — the evidence that many of the girls are responding in the same spirit. The adults are repelled by the publicness and the wholesaleness of this kind of wooing. They are disturbed that girls of supposed discrimination, at an age of supposed innocence, will adore such an inappropriate person. Fathers and other male citizens are also probably jealous of so phenomenally successful a lover.

But parents are mistaken when they interpret the responses of adolescent girls according to their own adult standards. I think there are three principal reasons, seemingly paradoxical, why a wholesome teen-age girl can respond to a performer who is offensive to her parents. She isn't actually doing anything wrong — she's just dreaming. The fact that he shows no noble side to his nature gets around any inhibition she may have against associating sex with a good person — he can just be a symbol of fascinating badness. At the very same time, the girl's relative innocence — as far as her conscious mind is concerned — allows her not to recognize what the performer is implying, or how she herself is responding at a subconscious level. This keeps her conscience clear.

You might say (perhaps inaccurately) that a girl can swoon in a theater only because she is not yet mature enough to swoon in the right boy's arms. After she has had the experience of being thoroughly in love with a real person she will have only a mild interest in a symbol of heavy romance on the stage.

Why don't boys carry on about sirens in the ways girls do about male singers? To a much milder degree they do. Boys of all ages have their enthusiasm for one popular seductress or another. But boys from early childhood have been taught to control and hide their feelings. I think that they also recognize their sexual feelings for what they are at an earlier stage of adolescence and so are less likely to reveal them ingenuously. Probably more important still is the fact that, to the average male, sex is predominantly a matter of initiative and activity rather than of passive response. He may be intrigued by a suggestive actress, but he won't be completely carried away by a performance in which he plays no active part.

☙ ☙ ☙

There are other factors that clinch the popularity of an idol of the teen-agers. They have a strong herd instinct. This is partly because each one is somewhat frightened by his changed body, changed interests, changed feelings. He is so strange to himself that he wonders at times whether he is normal. He craves to find similarities in hobbies, tastes, ideals with others his age. Erik Erikson, a profound student of adolescence, has pointed out that each individual at this age really finds himself in his friends. He is amazed and relieved and delighted when he discovers that someone else likes the same book, hates the same teacher, responds to the same music, has come to a similar philosophy of life. This need to share thoughts helps to explain why two girls who have been together all day and who have just parted rush to their phones to resume confidences. So if an adolescent girl can adore the same man that five million other girls adore, she feels sure she's normal, no matter what her parents may say.

And then if several thousand devotees are gathered in the presence of the idol in a theater, mass hysteria adds a pleasurable frenzy to the whole affair.

Another aspect of the herdlike behavior of teen-agers is their isolation from other age groups. They are trying hard to outgrow their own childishness, so they prefer to think of themselves as not children at all. Yet they are not really accepted into the adult world — at least not in our kind of civilization. In many simpler societies, adolescents go through certain initiation rites and then assume a dignified role in the life of the community, doing the same work as adults and participating in its important ceremonies. Even in America in colonial times some young men held positions of real responsibility by the age of twenty-one. But in America today we keep our adolescents in schools and colleges for years, where they go on learning more about the techniques of our civilization, with little opportunity to feel that they are full-fledged members of it. They not only don't hold regular jobs, they still have to live on allowances from their parents and submit to their judgment and authority. Our children agree with us that this is wise. But psychologically it keeps them from feeling grown up and it keeps them rebellious. So they make a virtue of their isolation from the adult world. They invent their own styles of dress and hairdo. They develop a language of their own. Rather hectically they foster their own hobbies and enthusiasms. They like having their own special idols in the field of entertainment. Then if it turns out that their idols happen to irritate their elders, that's an extra advantage.

I had better be sure that in my efforts to be reassuring I haven't misled some parent. I certainly don't mean that any degree of infatuation with an actor or hysteria in a theater is normal. In fact, there must be some highly unstable girls in the audiences we read about. I only mean that a teen-age girl can be a thoroughly wholesome person in other respects and still proclaim her love for a performer objectionable to her parents. This doesn't mean her judgment is not good in other respects, nor does it mean she won't have discrimination in regard to men later on.

But perhaps the reason I can be so philosophical is that I have no daughters.

THE MEANING OF
JUVENILE DELINQUENCY

*Various delinquencies are caused by
quite different kinds of disturbances —
either in the child's spirit or in
the family or in the neighborhood
or in the times.*

IT WORRIES parents to keep reading about the increase in juvenile delinquency that has occurred since World War II. And when they see in the paper that a shocking crime has been committed by a group of boys who come from "good families," they wonder whether this epidemic might not eventually infect *anybody* — even one of their supposedly wholesome children. In this chapter I'd like to try to shed some light on the meaning of delinquency so that parents won't feel quite so baffled and threatened by it.

The first point to make is that juvenile delinquency is a broad legal term which covers all the misbehavior for which children under eighteen can be brought to court — from truancy to murder. So the use of the term is unfortunate because it suggests that millions of our youth have been contaminated with evil, the cause and cure of which are unknown. It is as if every adult wrong from parking by a hydrant to starting a revolution were labeled adult turpitude in the daily papers, and viewed as an epidemic.

The next point is that various delinquencies are caused by quite different kinds of disturbances — either in the child's spirit or in the family or in the neighborhood or in the times. To think of them as if they had one cause is as misleading as it would be to consider all physical ailments such as cancer, contagious diseases, malnutrition, and broken bones as having only one cause. So I want to discuss, under separate headings, some of the types of misbehavior, and the sociological and psychological factors that are believed to cause them.

⟨ OUTWARD SOCIOLOGICAL FACTORS

In two different cities where I have lived, I've served on temporary citizens' committees on delinquency. At the first committee meeting in each place the prominent citizens sat around a large table listening to the reports of the seriousness of the situation, and gravely clicking their tongues. But after the meeting had been going on for an hour it was noticeable that a number of the committeemen were whispering to their neighbors and chuckling. They were admitting — a bit boastfully — that they had done some of these things themselves in their youth.

In fact, studies based on interviews with hundreds of ordinary male citizens have shown that nine out of ten of them committed acts during adolescence which were definitely illegal and would have got them into trouble if they had been caught. So, minor delinquency has probably always been extremely common. And the overwhelming majority of juvenile offenses are mild. One of those commonly engaged in by boys from all social levels is "malicious mischief" — dumping the garbage cans of unpopular neighbors, marking the walls of schools, letting air out of tires. Another is petty thievery — stealing fruit from a stand in front of a store or building materials from a neighborhood construction project. Such offenses express only mild destructiveness and defiance of property rights. Along with truancy and traffic violations, they do not necessarily imply any serious emotional disturbance in the individuals who commit them only occasionally, especially in neighborhoods where standards are not strict.

☙ ☙ ☙

A considerable majority of the delinquents who come to the attention of the courts are from families of lower economic and educational levels. But it is common knowledge that when a middle-class child causes trouble, the complaining citizen is more apt to turn to the child's parents than to the police, on the assumption that the parents, out of fairness and out of consideration for their reputation, will pay damages and make every effort to prevent recurrence. And when a complaint of not too serious a degree is brought to the police, it is their custom to attempt to deal with it directly with the parents, rather than make a record of it and bring it to court. Furthermore, in cases which are actually brought to court, the judge is more inclined to dismiss the case when the parents volunteer to make compensation and to deal with the child either by home punishment or boarding school or psychiatric treatment. So it's probably true that many middle-class youths manage to evade being listed in the delinquency statistics, which come only from court records.

But it is probably also true that a larger proportion of children of lower-income families commit delinquent acts and do so more often. If this is true, however, it does not mean that low income or little education in themselves mean lower morals. In many stable communities there is good evidence that there is no such association. But in large growing cities the lowest-income families are usually compelled to live in the most crowded, run-down parts of the town, with the poorest facilities for fostering good family living. These are also the least stable neighborhoods, where those at the bottom of the economic ladder are constantly moving in, and those who can afford to are moving out. Consequently neighborhood relationships and neighborhood leadership are minimal.

It is also true that some groups and individuals of limited education and income do not identify themselves — as other Americans do — with the predominant middle class. They have not yet acquired the strong middle-class beliefs in the importance of education, planning for the future, the channeling of aggression into competition and advancement, so they cannot teach these aspirations to their sons with great conviction. They feel themselves somewhat apart from this system. When their sons reach adolescence, with its urge to defiance, they are much more tempted to tangle with the authorities, or to refuse flatly to continue at school, than middle-class youths who have so much hope vested in the future. So it's not a difference in morals we're discussing but a difference in aspirations.

☙ ☙ ☙

A dramatic type of delinquency is the street gang which engages in various legal and illegal activities, including grim warfare with other gangs. These gangs have sprung up most often among the children of newcomers to American cities. In earlier generations the families immigrated from various European nations. Recently, gangs have appeared most often in Puerto Rican neighborhoods in our eastern cities, in Mexican neighborhoods in our Southwest, and in northern cities into which many Southern Negroes have moved. The fact that this same phenomenon has been repeated among groups coming from a dozen different parts of the world, with a great diversity of traditions and cultures behind them, shows that it is not due to the particular characteristics of any one racial or ethnic group. It is mainly caused by the conditions under which each new wave of settlers has had to live, and the attitude of other groups toward them.

As the newest arrivals and the least trained, each of these groups has had to take, in turn, the most menial jobs, received the lowest pay, occupied the poorest housing. More significantly still, they have been looked down on because of their poverty, "ignorance," and "strange ways," been discriminated against, been called uncomplimentary names. The parents have, to some degree, been frustrated by all the drastic adjustments they were called upon to make in coming from a rural background to raise a family in poverty in a strange city, and have sometimes been unable to provide their children with an atmosphere of security and self-respect. Often they have been alarmed to see their children picking up manners and attitudes and companions quite different from those which would have been considered proper in the old country, and have tried to interfere.

The children have felt, on the one hand, scorned by other groups in school and neighborhood. And yet, because they were taking on new American attitudes, they could not believe wholeheartedly in their parents' "old-fashioned" standards. (I remember an adolescent girl telling me how furiously resentful she felt when her Italian-born parents, following their traditions of respectability, refused to let her have dates in high school.) So in adolescence, when impatience with parents increases under any circumstances and aggressiveness is stirred up by glandular changes, some of the sons have cut themselves off from their families' control, and responded to the unfriendliness which they felt from other groups by forming tight-knit gangs with their own kind. Into these they have channeled their loyalty and bravery. Toward rival gangs they have channeled their accumulated hostility.

This is a one-sided description. I've been talking as though there were no defects in the characters of these boys, only the difficult sociological situation that confronts them. Actually there is a wide range in the characters of the boys in street gangs, from solid citizens to ruthless guys who have serious emotional problems and come from disturbed families.

To round out the picture, I should add that the great majority of families immigrating from European countries, Mexico, and Puerto Rico, and those moving from the South to northern cities, have proved to be law-abiding and productive people, and their sons have not needed gangs. When families from far away move into a community where there are already relatives and friends and compatriots from the old country, and where there are strong religious institutions and traditions of neighborhood leadership, they have the least trouble keeping their youth in line. There has been almost no delinquency, for instance, in the Chinese community in New York City, which is tightly knit. And individual families in which the parents are high-principled, adaptable, and have good relationships with their children can move anywhere without much fear of trouble.

(INNER PSYCHOLOGICAL CAUSES

Up to this point we have been discussing types of delinquency in which external sociological factors play a considerable part. From here on we'll deal with those largely the result of inner psychological disturbances. They vary greatly not only in severity but in their nature and cause. To make the distinctions between them clear I'll describe them as separate types and give them informal labels. But remember that this will be an oversimplification because there are usually several factors — psychological and sociological — operating to produce delinquency in any individual, and no one neat label covers the whole case.

The most important issue to the psychiatrist, the court, and society is whether a youth who has committed a moderately serious offense has a fundamental and extensive defect in his character such as cruelty, coldness, lack of conscience; or whether he is basically a human, reasonably conscientious person who can respond well under favorable circumstances but is disturbed in his feelings with regard to some particular situation.

I'd like to begin with three examples of delinquents of this latter type (sensible and dependable in most respects) who might be grouped under the heading "Mixed-up Unconscious Attitudes."

Kleptomaniacs have an irresistible compulsion, which they cannot explain, to steal certain objects which have no realistic usefulness to them. They are usually girls or women and they may have quite respectable reputations in other respects (in contrast to ordinary shoplifters with defective consciences who'll steal anything for profit). A kleptomaniac may steal dozens and dozens of fountain pens, for instance, even though she may have plenty of money to buy as many as she needs. The stolen objects represent some forbidden desire which is deeply repressed in her unconscious mind and which may be discovered through psychoanalysis.

Most Peeping Toms have no impulse to do harm to anyone and are, in other respects, law-abiding boys. But because of certain aspects of their upbringing they are too inhibited to approach girls in the usual teen-age ways, and all their intensifying sexual interests during adolescence become concentrated into a craving to look. There are other disturbances of sexual interest which belong in the same category, in the sense that there is no cruelty, no impulse to take advantage of another person by force. It is important to make this point because when a community becomes alarmed by a violent sex crime, there is an inclination to deal with every Peeping Tom or other mild deviant as if he were a fiend, too.

The third example I'll call "Need for Punishment." For instance, a boy commits a theft or robbery in such a clumsy way that he leaves clues all over the place and is easily caught.

Investigation reveals that he has conscientious parents who care a great deal about him. He may be well thought of by his friends and teachers. But at home he has been in a fuming, glowering conflict with his mother and father for a long time. They attribute his problems to the fact that they had considerable domestic strife when he was young. They feel very guilty about this and they blame themselves rather than him every time he acts up. Their submissiveness only encourages him to be more disagreeable to them — as if he believes they've done him wrong — but unconsciously he feels increasingly guilty about his abusiveness and senses the need to be controlled and punished. This is what has driven him, without his understanding it, to go out and provoke the authorities to do what his parents wouldn't do. Court psychiatrists are familiar with this need for punishment in a variety of cases.

💥 💥 💥

Next we can discuss a type of delinquency (that overlaps with other types) in which a child's conscience is fairly sound in most respects, but there is a specific gap in it. This permits him to commit one particular offense, perhaps again and again, which is out of keeping with the ostensible standards of the family. This aspect of delinquency was studied intensively by Dr. Adelaide Johnson and Dr. Stanislaus Szurek. They noticed that a parent, with whom they would be discussing the child's problem, would show indirect evidence of a suppressed impulse to indulge in the same kind of misbehavior. In the psychiatric treatment of the child they would find that he was picking up the parent's hidden attitude. Three simple examples will give you an idea of what they meant.

A mother suspects that the jackknife her son is playing with was stolen from a store. When with a little grilling she gets him to confess, her next impulsive question is: "Did anyone see you?" Of course this is not the line of thought of a moral parent, who should be entirely concerned at this point with correcting the child and helping him make amends. Instead it shows a degree of identification with the thief, and tips him off that the parent gives at least partial permission if the theft is successful.

A father is complaining about the fact that his small son, who is present, has run away from home a half dozen times. Then, as he describes the ingenuity of the boy in covering vast distances on each trip before he is caught, the father's tone becomes increasingly proud. This show of approval, of which the father is not aware, more than offsets his official disapproval.

A mother is haranguing her daughter about staying out late with a boy and ends up by declaring that she knows the girl has stopped at nothing. It so happens that this is not true — it's the mother's fantasy. But it is an indication to the girl of what her mother expects and thus is a kind of permission for the future. Drs. Johnson and Szurek pointed out that in such cases as these the defect in the child's conscience really corresponds to, and is caused by, a forbidden desire on the parent's part which the parent manages to suppress in himself but enjoys vicariously through his child.

So it's a sign of potential trouble ahead (which calls for expert help) when parents say — not jokingly — that they think their child is heading for delinquency or that they are helpless in controlling him. Such statements indicate either that the parents, without realizing it, are giving the child permission, or have some intense guiltiness toward him which is blocking normal discipline and will continue to do so.

☙ ☙ ☙

Now we can come to the delinquents who have some fundamental impairment of character. We might first dispose of the ones with the most severe distortions of personality. These are fortunately very few, but because of the vicious nature of their crimes they cause consternation.

For example, three boys murder in cold blood a person who has not harmed them, who in fact means nothing to them. Yet they do not appear crazy in the usual sense. Their only explanation is that they did it for a thrill. One can be quite sure that such a cruel, perverse act is never committed by individuals who are emotionally or morally normal, even though they may have seemed like ordinary people to casual acquaintances. Anybody who had known one of them well would be able to give evidences of unusual meanness and coldness going back to early childhood. Furthermore, long familiarity with the family, or psychiatric investigation, would reveal that the parents, no matter how "respectable" they seemed, had treated this boy with the lack of human kindness that he shows toward others — not necessarily beatings or other crude forms of cruelty. Meanness can be carried out with velvet gloves.

Another somewhat different example of severe character distortion is the youth who commits a gruesome crime, perhaps a "sex murder." Yet it is reported that he had never been a bad boy before but had, moreover, established a reputation for unusual virtue in terms of attendance at Sunday School or Scout meetings. However, one should not be fooled by the newspaper reporter's desire for drama and contrast. It may well be true that such a boy had not previously got into any scrapes, but you can be sure that he was not the usual warmhearted, outgoing American boy. He probably had noticeable peculiarities in his personality throughout childhood but was able to conform to the requirements of school and the neighborhood. Then the inner tensions of adolescence broke through his fragile self-control, in somewhat the same way that they push a few other maladjusted adolescents over the brink into insanity. Here, too, one would have been able to see, all along, a distinctly atypical parent-child relationship.

☙ ☙ ☙

We still have left to consider the largest category of chronic delinquents, those who *repeatedly* commit offenses of mild to moderate degree — chronic truancy, running away, theft, robbery, stealing of cars for an evening's fun, sexual promiscuity and prostitution on the part of girls. The majority of these youths can be thought of as having *generally* impaired consciences as a result of gross neglect in early childhood. The traditional term for them is psychopathic personality, and they are defined as shallow, irresponsible, impulsive, demanding individuals who don't learn from experiences. There are at least a few mild psychopaths in every community. You may remember one in your school, or may have been frustrated as an adult in trying to deal with one.

I can make the picture more vivid by describing the kind of sailors I had for my patients in a prison ward in the Navy. They were awaiting final discharge as worthless for military service because they had repeatedly been absent without leave for longer and longer periods (and committed other offenses), despite increasingly severe punishments. The usual excuse was simply, "I had to go over the hill. I asked for leave and they wouldn't give it to me." On the prison ward they were always demanding something: better food and more meat, though they had a good diet compared to civilians; more opportunities to telephone their girl friends; more recreational activities (with each of which they promptly became bored); quicker action on their discharge papers. When the red tape would catch up with a man who had been absent for six months, and the pay allotment to his family would be cut off, he would come to me indignantly. I'd tell him that no organization pays a man who has long since deserted his job, but this wouldn't embarrass him. In an outraged tone he would shout, "How does the Navy expect my family to live?" It would never occur to him that he himself owed any obligation.

How does a person get to be a psychopath? Generally speaking it happens because nobody loved him the first few years of his life. The histories of most of the sailors on my ward were monotonously the same. One man's mother died when he was born and his father turned him over to a relative or to a neighbor who, he still remembers, didn't want him. Another's father died or deserted, his mother had to go to work, and she left him in an understaffed orphanage. This is the kind of broken home that really produces delinquency, where the parents are not only separated (by death or divorce or desertion) but where the remaining parent makes poor provision for the child, visits him irregularly, goes back on promises, and in general leaves him with the feeling of being unwanted anywhere. It can also happen right in the child's own family if nobody cares for him.

(The simple fact that a home is broken does not mean that psychopathic personalities or delinquents will be produced. Most widowed and divorced mothers — and fathers too — who are devoted to their children make suitable provision for their care so that the children feel well loved.)

By the time a seriously neglected child reaches school he is commonly a tense, restless, shallow person. He takes little interest in schoolwork because he has no model of a fond parent to emulate, no particular ambition, no capacity to devote himself to learning projects. Never having been a real member of a family, he has no feeling of wanting to be a part of the group in his classroom. Never having known the satisfying security of being approved of, he doesn't dread the loss of approval that comes from misbehavior; punishment doesn't make him feel contrite, only resentful. Never having known the joy of being loved, he doesn't try to evoke it from others. Since no one ever gave him anything important, he has nothing real to give, either. So, as a pupil, he follows his impulses, is often in trouble, spends a lot of time sitting in the principal's office, plays hooky, is apt eventually to fail of promotion a couple of times, and quits school for good as soon as he can get away with it. He has no real friends.

A psychopath may imagine that when he leaves school and goes to work he'll be on easy street, but all his deficiencies accompany him onto the job. He proves an unreliable, inattentive, unco-operative worker, and either is fired or quits every job within a few weeks.

I have been describing full-fledged psychopaths, but there are many of lesser degree. They don't grow up only in obviously broken or underprivileged or indifferent homes. It's important to remember that some children from comfortable homes, where the parents are respectable or even prominent citizens, may also be brought up without deep affection or devotion. The neglect may be less obvious because the family maintains a conventional front and appears to provide the child with everything that society considers right. In some cases the parents, out of a vague sense of guilt, try to make up for their lack of love by heaping possessions and privileges on the child. A dramatic example of this is the good-for-nothing teen-ager who has been given an expensive car.

☙ ☙ ☙

Can we draw any positive conclusions from the discouraging array of disturbances that I've been discussing in this chapter? I think there are several:

1. A great majority of the acts that make up the delinquency statistics are quite minor offenses which do not necessarily point to any emotional disturbance in the youths who commit them.

2. Delinquency does not appear out of the blue. The children who become chronic delinquents or who commit serious offenses have been showing signs of maladjustment from early childhood and could have been helped.

3. If a child receives warm love and steady guidance from his parents — even though they get mad or discouraged with him at times — he will be acquiring a sense of belonging and a conscience which will keep him from committing any serious offenses in adolescence and make him in adulthood a responsible member of society.

Some of the implications of these points will be discussed in the later chapters on treatment and prevention of delinquency.

WHY ADOLESCENTS
MISBEHAVE

*Storms rumbling under the surface in
the search for a new self.*

◆◆◆◆◆◆◆◆◆◆◆◆◆◆◆◆◆◆◆◆◆◆◆◆◆◆◆◆◆◆◆◆◆◆

WHY IS IT that so much of the behavior of children which offends the community is concentrated in the adolescent years? The sharpest peak in the delinquency statistics occurs between the ages of fifteen and seventeen.

First of all, there is a considerable difference in the offenses of girls and boys. Boys get into trouble mainly through aggressive acts such as stealing and destructiveness, and by defying the school attendance laws. A few of them are prone to violence or cruelty. Only rarely do you hear of girls who are capable of such open aggressiveness. The majority of girls in court are there, on the compaint of their parents, because of sexual behavior which the parents can't control or because of running away from home. In other words, girls alarm and defy their parents whereas boys threaten society.

In some cases girls become involved in disapproved sexual behavior mainly because they have been unloved and neglected

since infancy and as a result have no standards which exert control over their impulses. In other cases the motivation is more
complex. There are girls who protest too loudly to court workers
that their parents give them no affection or treat them harshly,
which suggests that one of their deeper motives is to hurt and
shame their parents. And when a girl talks most bitterly against
her father for showing her no approval, you can see that she has
found a perfect revenge in flaunting an affair with a man whom
her father detests. Psychiatric study shows that the intensified
rivalry that adolescent daughters and their mothers often feel
toward each other helps to explain the particular way girls get
into trouble. There are cases in which it becomes clear that a
girl suddenly, foolishly, defiantly exposes herself to pregnancy,
with a boy or man who means little to her, when she discovers
that her mother is going to have a baby. Another girl goes looking for trouble when her divorced or widowed mother acquires
an intimate man friend. Social workers in homes for illegiti-
mately pregnant girls are familiar with the common problem of
the girl who angrily storms out and involves herself with a man
after her mother has unjustifiably accused her of immorality.
In such cases as these (and I am not including other, undefiant
types of illegitimate pregnancy), the adolescence of the girl does
not create a problem primarily because of her increasing interest
in other men and boys. Rather it intensifies all the positive and
negative feelings she has had for her parents since early childhood. Most specifically it heightens her competitiveness with her
mother and convinces her that now it's *her* turn to have the attention of men, with all that this implies. And when a daughter
begins to turn into an attractive young thing it may arouse in her
mother unconscious feelings of envy.

Even in smoothly running families you can often see subtle
signs of this rivalry. An adolescent daughter may act quite indignant when told that her mother is pregnant, as if the mother
should be way beyond "that sort of thing"; or be sharply critical
if she thinks her mother is being too kittenish in clothes or manner; or make a great show of how much better she understands

and treats her father than her mother does. This reminds us of the rivalry of the three-to-five-year-old girl for her father's attention, which is partly suppressed after the age of six. Then under the urging of the glandular changes it emerges again temporarily in the teen years. This helps to explain why some adolescent girls are so intensely disagreeable to their mothers. They feel antagonistic, but they also feel guilty about it and are asking for punishment. It also explains why an occasional girl acts outrageously critical of her father: she may be trying to cover her positive feelings with negative ones, just as adults sometimes do when unwilling to admit attraction; and at the same time she may be provoking him to pay her some rough attention. I remember a girl from a conventional family who kept screaming at her father that he was a hen-pecked weakling, until he found himself slapping her in the face. He was ashamed of this act, but surprised to see that it didn't offend her at all. Eventually the adolescent discovers movie actors and entertainers and boys in the neighborhood who absorb her romantic feelings, and then she gradually badgers her father and mother less.

Running away from home appeals to a girl who does not have a good relationship with parents or a stable personality, but who is not bold enough to be openly defiant at home. It may satisfy several of her desires. It offers the lure of romantic adventure. It tortures the parents with anxiety and makes the neighbors wonder how mean the parents have been. In the child's fantasies, it may signify a search for ideal parent substitutes who will provide boundless love, understanding, approval, possessions, privileges, and ask nothing in return.

Running away is a very exaggerated response to the common complaint of adolescents, even in stable families, that their parents don't understand them. I remember a magazine article which reported on a questionnaire survey of thousands of adolescents of various ages. It showed that there was a sharp peak in the frequency with which they complained of not being understood, around fifteen years of age. At younger and older ages there was much less of this feeling. The author concluded that something drastic needed to be done by American parents to overcome this lack of understanding. To me, it doesn't seem logical that parents who understand their children well enough at thirteen and eighteen will develop any sudden gap in their knowledge of them when they are fifteen. Rather it must be a normal aspect of middle adolescence to feel misunderstood by parents. I think it is really a reflection of the child's pulling away from his parents. He is cutting off old attachments and dependency in order to achieve a sounder independence. And I think it's quite natural that he should have to blame this sense of alienation on the parents.

In a similar way, there are shy adolescents who are so scared of not being able to measure up to the new demands of social and romantic life that they don't dare participate, but who'd never admit it in a thousand years. Instead, they insist that it is their parents who won't let them go to parties or on dates.

🌾 🌾 🌾

In boys many of the manifestations of adolescent tension are different from those of girls. A basic concern in all boys and men is to convince the world — and, more importantly, to convince themselves — of their virility. Virility in the specifically sexual sphere is only one aspect of this concern. It is more evident in the male's ambition to be able to compete successfully in his occupation, in skills, in strength, in courage, in toughness, in earning money, in providing for his family.

The need to prove his manliness is particularly compelling for a male in adolescence. His development has come quite abruptly. He feels embarrassed by his closeness still to childhood. He is frustrated by the fact that in the eyes of his parents, his teachers, and the law he is still a dependent minor. There are not many opportunities for a convincing demonstration of his prowess, except perhaps in the case of the outstanding athlete. The automobile becomes particularly important for the adolescent as a symbol of power and as a way to impress girls, to demonstrate skill and bravery, to compete with other drivers, even if he has to risk his life or break the law to do so. Cigarette smoking in boys doesn't start as a habit or as a taste — it is an assertion of manliness and perhaps also a defiance of the parents' rules.

Well-adjusted youths who are successful in extracurricular activities and in dating have sufficient basis to bide their time while they dream optimistically about the future. Other boys, who have less aptitude in these areas but who have parents who set high ideals, can discipline their drives into academic, intellectual, scientific, artistic pursuits.

But the balance is different for boys growing up with parents who have no conviction about the importance of education and the planning of a career, or, worse still, with parents who show little devotion to their children and expect little from them. Then the adolescent's impulse to prove his virility at once is given freer reign, and it is at least a partial motive in much of the truancy, mischief, and theft of this age period. One boy suggests an illegal escapade to the group, and the need of each to prove himself in his own eyes and in the eyes of the others urges him to agree. The defiance of authorities is an integral part of the satisfaction.

When discussing the delinquency of girls I emphasized the exaggerated rivalry between unstable daughters and their mothers, and the revenge of daughters against their unattentive fathers. Is there anything which corresponds to this in boys? We know that a boy feels rivalry with his father for the attention of his mother in the three-to-five-year-old period and that the anxieties aroused by this rivalry cause the whole matter to be vigorously repressed into the boy's unconscious mind. In most boys, this results in an intense taboo which makes them shun expressions of physical affection between themselves and their mothers, not only in the latency period between six and twelve years but even more in adolescence. You don't see many boys patting their mothers on the head or calling them by pet names, the way girls often do to their fathers. Boys are more inclined to recoil when their mothers try to show them any physical fondness. They may be sharply critical when their mothers' skirts slip up too high or if they think their dresses are too revealing. Some of them are so anxious to cover up any sense of attraction to their mothers that, at times, they pick on them relentlessly for almost everything they say or do.

There is lots of indirect evidence that the old rivalry with the father, strongly repressed, persists through boyhood and into adulthood. It comes nearest to the surface in competitiveness with the father in regard to games, skills, success in careers. In most families a boy's awe of his father is much stronger than a girl's awe of her mother, so he is less inclined to argue with him or provoke him. When he's mad at his old man he's more apt to sulk or mutter under his breath.

It often happens, too, that a boy's subconscious fear of antagonizing his father may cause him to suppress his awareness of his own irritation toward him. Instead he takes out the irritation on his mother (or on teachers), flares up at her harmless remarks, picks arguments with her over nothing. You may well be skeptical when I glibly make a statement like this. What kind of evidence is there? An adolescent or young man enters psychoanalytic treatment because of some life-adjustment problem such as failure in school or job, or inability to get along with people. He is convinced that much of his difficulty is caused by what he considers his mother's domination, and that he gets along excellently with his eminently reasonable father. Even outsiders would agree that the father-son relationship is warm and mutually respectful. But when the patient begins to relate his dreams (which come from his unconscious mind), they repeatedly portray situations in which he is being threatened or taken advantage of by a powerful man who is obviously his father or has characteristics of his father. (If a motherlike figure appears in the dreams she is usually playing an affectionate, sympathetic role.) And when the patient, by "free association," thinks of what the various details in a dream remind him, they keep leading him back to half-forgotten episodes in earlier childhood in which he dreaded his father's anger or fiercely resented his father's authority or advantages or unfairness. If the treatment is successful in giving the patient an understanding and control over his deeper feelings, it will show up in at least three changes. He will solve the school or job problem. He will quit blaming his mother. He will be aware of occasional realistic differences of opinion between himself and his father and not be afraid of standing up for his own views even if this may lead to a hot argument.

A rebellious adolescent boy may go with a certain girl in part because he senses that his mother won't like her, but he usually doesn't have such a need to use his affair against his parents that he makes a public scandal of it. And though a mother may have a strong impulse to break it up, she can't persuade her husband to call in the police (as he may do in the case of a defiant daughter). There isn't the same urgency in parents about protecting the virtue of boys, because there is still a double standard, and the boy is thought of as able to live down his early indiscretions.

For the same reason, there is less panic when an older boy runs away from home. If he has been difficult for some time and is sixteen or more, the parents in a family that is not committed to higher education may just assume he is better off on his own. I remember how impressed I was in the Navy to learn how a number of my patients who came from mountaineer families reached manhood. A boy of about sixteen years would find himself for the first time refusing angrily to do what his father commanded. When his father would double up his fist to teach him a lesson, the boy, without premeditation, would knock him down. Then he'd realize that he was too grown up to stay home any longer, and go off to find a job somewhere else.

The rivalry of sons with their fathers may not often cause open family turmoil but it very frequently disturbs an adolescent boy's academic progress, in families with high educational standards. A boy in high school or college, who has good intelligence and who in the past has been co-operative and ambitious, begins to argue with teachers or provoke them. Or he may slump badly in most of his subjects. In a heart-to-heart talk he'll say that he's sorry, that he doesn't know what's the matter, but that he just can't seem to buckle down. Another boy will give every evidence of trying hard and being very concerned but he truly can't make his mind stay on his books any more or he can't comprehend a certain subject. In the process of psychoanalysis it may become gradually clear that, deep in his unconscious mind, some aspect of his rivalry with his father (with roots going back to early childhood) is causing part of the difficulty. He may be rebelling against his father's authority or his father's plans for him. He may, without any realization of it, be afraid that he won't do as well as his father, or else that he might do better and thus make his father resentful.

♩ ♩ ♩

We are accustomed to emphasizing the rebellion against parents. But the rebellion is only the prelude to the more difficult problem which the youth has to face — finding what sort of person he wants to be as an adult. What kind of work will he want to do? What attitudes and interests will he have? What type of spouse will he seek? This is the problem of identity which Erik Erikson has done so much to clarify and which is the theme of his book *Young Man Luther*.*

For many young people this is not a smooth process of slipping into an obvious niche. It's more like an intermittent storm in the emotions which lasts for several years. The adolescent has to emancipate himself from parents in order to become a reasonably independent and effective adult. Yet he is surely made from his parents, not just in flesh and blood but in tastes, ideals, and manners. So, in a sense, he has to tear apart some of the most intimate components of his personality. Eventually, in most cases, he feels free enough, certain enough to be able to select

* W. W. Norton & Company, New York, 1958.

the pieces which suit him (even if they happen to have come from his parents), and fit them together again for the adult life he has chosen.

In this slow process the feelings are turbulent and changeable. There are quick enthusiasms (often for unsuitable interests and friends), deep discouragement, bland evasion, panicky groping, sudden anger.

Adolescents instinctively try on a variety of personalities (including disapproved ones) like clothes, to test for fit and appearance and satisfaction. Then there is agonizing self-consciousness about whether the impression made on outsiders is what was so eagerly intended, or whether the effect was just silly. They often have to seek new friendships and dates, not because they are fickle but because they change substantially within themselves over short periods of time.

In the adolescents who become so bewildered in the search for a new self that they have a dreadful feeling of losing what little identity they still have, there may be a sudden, hectic conversion to religion or even a serious nervous breakdown. Erikson has pointed out that some adolescents, dead set against becoming like their parents but still entirely confused about a constructive alternative, settle temporarily on the exact opposite of the parents' expectations. A boy raised in a conservative family becomes an ostentatious radical. A very properly raised girl runs away and associates with disreputable women. The beatnik stubbornly reverses every detail of the manner in which he was raised, but then dons the uniform of the cult to be sure that he belongs to something.

Erikson has suggested that a gang may be an important refuge and outlet for certain youths from those minority groups which are newly arrived in our cities and subject to discrimination and scorn. Their parents are usually the ones who are having the greatest difficulty adjusting to the new environment in terms of succeeding at jobs, in keeping family relationships close and calm. As a result the children have little motive to identify proudly with their parents. Yet they can't very well identify with the dominant urban American culture which rejects them. The impulse which makes them come together in gangs where they can feel that they are understood and respected, where they can gain a sense of belonging and learn co-operation, is often basically healthy.

Gang formation is an exaggeration of the clannishness of most adolescents. They are trying to emancipate themselves from their dependence on their parents. But they aren't yet — in our kind of civilization — accepted as full-fledged working members of the adult community. So they emphasize the separateness of their age group by wearing their own style of clothes, having their special recreations and idols, even developing their own vocabulary. In these ways they buttress their weakened sense of identity as individuals during the transition.

☙ ☙ ☙

I think it's helpful for parents of normal children to have an idea of some of the storms which may be rumbling under the surface at this age so that they know how to take their cues.

The struggle for independence does not mean that parents should suddenly stop providing firm guidance. The adolescent is not so much fighting the parents as he is fighting his deeply ingrained dependence on them. He needs to know where they stand so that he will be in a better position to take his own stand. He secretly borrows from their strength of purpose until he can develop his own. All adolescents acknowledge that they need and want guidance, but they seldom say this to their own parents. At the same time, parents should be reasonable in their willingness to discuss issues. It's important that they show a basic trust in their children's characters even when they are laying down regulations for parties and dates.

The fact that a mother knows that her daughter's uppityness expresses a normal rivalry doesn't mean that she should turn the other cheek. That only arouses guilt and further provocation.

And, after all, the father does belong, romantically speaking, to the mother, not the daughter, so the mother has nothing to apologize for. She fosters her daughter's continued growth and stability by expecting courtesy and co-operation from her.

A good father doesn't have to shy away from his teen-age daughter. She needs his friendliness, approval, interest in her concerns. But he will help her to gain independence and maturity by dropping the cuddliness with which he may have treated her earlier. He should certainly avoid the trap, that she may unconsciously set, of forming a close alliance with her which excludes the mother or which is used to tease the mother and undermine her authority. To see clearly that her father and mother have a relationship of mutual devotion and respect which can't be subverted will aid a daughter to make the right marriage herself, and to trust herself and her own future daughters as they grow up.

In the raising of a boy through the adolescent years, a father obviously has a more important and more extensive role to play than in earlier childhood when the mother could be a satisfactory arbiter of what he was to wear to school, when he should come home, how he was to treat his sister. Now that he is so close to manhood, a boy feels that his mother is hopelessly out of touch with the traditions and practices of the male world and that it's inappropriate and undignified for him to have to take much of his guidance from her. But to bring about this shift of authority, it won't work if a father who has previously left most of the discipline to his wife continues to hang back, and then reverses the decisions she has made. He must move in and assume leadership as the issues first come up.

The fact that a boy at this age may be inclined to take out on his mother the antagonism he would normally feel for his father is an important added reason why a mother should not have to be the disciplinarian now. But an occasional mother may have difficulty giving up the fussing and bossing role. She acts as a lightning rod for her son's irritation. Whenever they are in the house together there are constant flashes and rumblings. The disputes come so fast that it's hard for the father to get in between. So a mother should try hard not to raise issues that can more properly be handled by her husband (though of course she should not submit to spontaneous rudeness and criticism from the boy). The father should be prompt to decide issues raised by the son, and to reprimand him when necessary. This is partly to keep his wife from becoming embroiled. More importantly, it is to keep clear in the boy's feelings that it's with men that he has to solve most of his authority problems in life, but that these aren't too difficult to manage if they're recognized for what they are.

WHY HAS DELINQUENCY
INCREASED?

Standards have relaxed and a number of
disturbing trends have appeared.

AN URGENT question today about delinquency is why the figures have kept increasing since the war.

A few professional people have argued that there is no proof that the actual amount is larger. They believe that the seeming increase could be accounted for by heightened public awareness of the problem, and by greater activity on the part of police, social agencies, and teachers. In a similar way the mounting figures for many physical and mental diseases are believed to have been brought about, in part, by improved diagnosis and more accurate reporting.

It's true that the police will make the statistics go up by being stricter — by bringing charges instead of just giving reprimands. And when the press and the public become alarmed, the pressure is on the police to crack down. Certainly it is impossible to compare accurately the figures of one year with another, of one place with another. The laws are different in each locality, they are changed from time to time, and the enforcement varies greatly.

However, most experts believe that the true incidence has gone up in the years following the war — gone up a lot. No one has any proof of the causes. Your opinions or mine are as valid as anyone else's, as long as they conform to the statistics.

Some of the figures are certainly food for speculation. The incidence of delinquency is highest in cities. But the *proportional* increase has been more rapid, in recent years, in towns.

We are apt to think of the increase as being an American problem, but most European countries have experienced the same thing. Russia has an undisclosed number of delinquents, and the Russian press has been complaining indignantly in recent times about "hooliganism," even among the children of professional people and officials.

᛭ ᛭ ᛭

The statistics point to a correlation with the economic state of the nation. The cases go up during prosperity, down during depression. We can only guess at the underlying meaning. The best explanation, to me, is that families are sobered and united by adversity, that human beings usually do their best when faced with a challenge, as long as it is not too overwhelming. But when money comes easily, the bonds and controls are relaxed. Each member of the family is more able to follow his own interests. Parents themselves are less apt to set such a high example of devotion to family welfare. And it's harder for them to keep adolescents firmly in line when the latter can earn enough in spare time to be financially semi-independent.

Another factor that comes into play when prosperity has climbed to higher levels than ever before is that millions of parents are bringing up their children in circumstances markedly different from those in which they were reared themselves. Perhaps as children they had needed to devote much of their time to essential work in the home or on the farm, do without playthings, wear old clothes, waste nothing, contribute to the family a part of their earnings when they went to work. Then if they bring up their own children under conditions where none of these obligations is necessary, they may be uncertain about what to require of them, and end up asking too little. In fact there is sometimes a temptation to shower the children with possessions, treats, privileges which they don't need and don't even ask for, as if the parents were trying to make up to them for their own early deprivations.

A purely mechanical factor that must have played a considerable part in freeing youth from control, both in the practical and in the moral sense, has been the multiplication of automobiles. When I think of their availability for getting out from under the eyes of parents, for showing off, for dates and pickups and abductions, for "borrowing," for running away from home, for getting away from the scene of the crime, it makes me realize how limited the facilities used to be in the olden days for doing wrong or going wrong.

Two other changes in American living have been the population shift from country to city, and the mobility of families. They shift neighborhoods in the same city as their fortunes improve, move to other regions in search of better jobs, get transferred by companies — with a frequency and casualness that would have been considered fantastic a couple of generations ago. There is not much doubt that one factor which makes parents particular about their own and their children's behavior is a natural desire to be well thought of by particular neighbors. If parents who are not very strict within themselves don't expect to be in a community for long, or assume that half the neighbors will be gone in a couple of years, or have so many neighbors that they know none of them, there will not be quite the same urgency about building a good reputation.

In a similar way, travelers and men in the armed forces often behave less properly than they do in their own towns. I remember an idealistic professor telling me about how, as a member of the army invading the enemy's country in World War II, he enjoyed breaking windows and "liberating" useful articles, without any of the inner prohibitions or pangs of conscience that would have stopped him or made him miserable at home.

This normal letdown which comes from being away from relatives and neighbors can be seen dramatically in the unusually high rates of crime among single men who migrate to our industrial centers looking for work.

An unexpected and disconcerting result of large urban redevelopment projects has been a temporary increase in the rates of delinquency both in the families who have to pull up their roots and move to other neighborhoods when their old housing is pulled down, and in the families who come in to occupy the new housing, in which they have no roots or relationships in the beginning.

🙚 🙚 🙚

I suspect that when we search for the causes of the increase in delinquency in the years since World War II, we ought not to limit ourselves to factors which have been operating only that long. Other trends which started much earlier are probably contributing still.

World War I called millions of American men into the armed services and women into industry, with high hopes of saving the world. But the war and particularly its aftermath proved disillusioning. The decade of the 1920's was marked by a cynicism unprecedented in this country. Literature veered toward harsh realism. Novelists drew characters who posed as moral or religious people, and then exposed them as hypocrites. Biographers "debunked" the heroes of history. The constitutional amendment prohibiting alcoholic beverages was flouted widely and gleefully, and this encouraged disrespect for all laws. Certain aspects of American innocence and idealism took a pounding in those years from which they've never entirely recovered. The aftermath of World War II has also been disillusioning for youth, with a war in Korea coming so soon afterward, and international tensions still rising. But the letdown has been less severe than in the 1920's, perhaps because the expectations had never been so unrealistically lofty. A proportion of today's delinquency is attributed to the feeling in youths that they are entitled to some wildness before they submit to the army's discipline.

Throughout this period since 1918 the molding of the ideals of youth, which was formerly carried out by parents and church without much outside competition (especially in farm and small-town families), increasingly has had to be shared with the movies, broadcasting, popular literature, and advertising, which have quite different ideas to sell. And parents, on their part, have been exposed to new concepts of child development which have the effect on some of them of decreasing the self-assurance and firmness which they've needed more than ever, perhaps, to guide their children through these unstable times.

〆 〆 〆

In addition to the specific social trends we've discussed, we should probably take into account the pendulum swings — the tides — that seem to influence all the affairs of mankind. Styles in clothes have always changed, even before there was an organized clothing industry to guide them. In the histories of architecture, music, and literature there have been repeated alternations between classical restraint and romantic imaginativeness. Phases of waxing and waning have regularly followed each other in the intensity of religious beliefs and in the strictness of morality. When a trend appears, it continues to gain adherents and momentum for an extended period. Eventually it goes too far. People become bored or irritated or alarmed, depending on the nature of the case, and a reaction sets in.

I think that one of the longer roots of today's high delinquency goes back beyond World War I to the reaction which set in, around the turn of the century, against Victorianism. In that earlier period the official standards were painfully high. There was a concerted effort to ignore and deny all the cruder aspects of humanity. Manners were formal. Dress was somber. Women were meant to be innocent, modest, delicate, deferential to their husbands. Parents, indissolubly bound, were supposed to set an upright example. They were always right just because they were parents. Children were expected to be most unnaturally good. No allowance was made for the normality of greediness, balkiness, jealousy, angriness, childhood sexuality. The model child presented in some nineteenth-century stories was so proper and sanctimonious that he gives us goose flesh today.

There has been a revolt against all these values which has not only persisted but progressed right up to the present. The informalizing of behavior and dress are plain to see. The change in the status of women has been enormous (and perhaps upsetting to all concerned). The skyrocketing figures for divorce show that something drastic has happened to the concept of marriage in many people's minds. The Kinsey reports documented the change that has occurred in the sexual mores of adults as well as adolescents. In regard to the care of children, the reaction has sometimes gone beyond the ideal of understanding them in order to guide them more wisely, to a timid or casual overpermissiveness.

You may think I'm being a prophet of doom in calling attention to all the disturbing influences and the relaxation of standards in this half century. That's not my idea. My immediate purpose has been only to suggest some explanations for the increase in delinquency. I'd say that there are enough plausible reasons so that we shouldn't be surprised or bewildered or even too discouraged that a somewhat larger than usual minority of our youth has gone off the beaten path. In fact, when we consider all things, it seems remarkable that a greater proportion of our youth than ever before is in school, studying harder in most cases, showing, I think, greater maturity in their understanding of the world than their parents and grandparents did. I don't mean that I believe we are doing as much as we could to help them, as I'll discuss in following chapters.

The apparent lowering of certain of our standards is not necessarily a loss. Many of the nineteenth-century ideals were stuffy, blind, untrue, more cramping than inspiring. They had to be corrected before we could move ahead. It's only too bad that the revolt had to carry us to extremes in some respects — just as the revolt in certain adolescents makes them strive temporarily for the very opposite of what their parents exemplify. In regard to all the technical and social changes that are influencing our way of life, we can't ignore them and we shouldn't accept them passively. We will have to watch where they are taking us and make sensible efforts to control them. That will require a set of workable beliefs — spiritual and practical — about what kind of a world we will want to leave for our children and how we should rear them in order to make the best of it.

☙ ☙ ☙

Meanwhile I'll express a few opinions about the management of normal adolescents in these complex times. I think one of the common problems today is that some parents have been made hesitant by changing customs and by the fear of being called too strict and old-fashioned. Teen-agers soon discover this gap in their parents' armor. They probe it often to see whether they can push the limits back. Through it they learn to send well-aimed reproaches. They act as if they wanted to throw off all controls. But they'd be frightened if they succeeded. Really they are debating within themselves, a good deal of the time, whether they have the sophistication to be able to play some grown-up role or other. It necessitates, perhaps, getting permission to go out with certain people or to visit an unusual place or to stay out late. When parents hesitate or refuse, children start the reproaches. They'd like to get permission, on general principles. But if they can't, they want to pin *all* the blame indignantly on the parents, to conceal from themselves their lack of self-confidence. So mothers and fathers should learn to brush reproaches aside and settle each request on its merits.

A present-day example of a social style that has taken the bit in its teeth is the custom of going steady in early adolescence. Just where it came from nobody seems to know. Certainly most parents haven't encouraged it. A majority of the boys and girls involved are not that ready for romance, and they are obviously not mature enough to make such a narrowing choice. Yet the more the movement has spread, the more it has seemed to compel other shyer and younger children to conform to the pattern — perhaps for social security at parties, perhaps to prove that they are as successful in winning partners as the next ones. To the parents, the picture of two children doggedly dancing with each other all evening seems such a waste of the party's gaiety. They worry that the constancy of the relationship will prevent a wide acquaintance with others, and might lead to an intimacy that could have serious social and emotional consequences. I think parents who feel that early dating and going steady are inappropriate are within their rights — and also doing their child a favor — to interfere tactfully. It isn't necessary to belittle a child's romance or his maturity. In fact, the parents can act pleased that he or she has found someone so appealing. But they can explain that they consider it unwise to make any commitment to one person so many years before possible marriage, and that the children should arrange dates only as members of a larger group.

Parents can keep track of the kinds of movies being shown in the neighborhood, and ask their children not to attend crude presentations. Even if the children secretly disobey, they will have a cue as to how to judge the show.

Parents are being sensible and helpful when they make it a practice to inquire who their child's companions will be at

To p. 284

parties and on dates (and greet them if practical), to approve the plans (including the matter of who is to drive), to set the hours. This custom can be started as a matter of course at the beginning of adolescence, and then continued without apology for several years until the child has proved his maturity.

It's almost inevitable that children will protest vehemently at times: that no one else has to come home so early, that the place they want to go is as respectable as a church, that the unknown character who is going to drive is an Eagle Scout. The parents' best defense is to keep in touch with the parents of their children's friends, and to devote P.T.A. meetings to discussion of such matters. It's not that any one family should feel obliged to follow the majority. But it's very helpful to get a perspective from hearing the views and practices of parents of various kinds. It's often a surprise and a pleasure to find that most of them share your point of view (contrary to reports from your children), and that everyone is ready to come to a neighborhood agreement. Such a code is a comfort to the children, too, because it reassures them that they will not be ridiculously out of line.

THE TREATMENT OF DELINQUENCY

There is a lot of ignorance and indifference to be overcome.

WHEN A YOUTH has been caught — by a neighbor for instance — in some illegal act, there are several possible outcomes. If the neighbor notifies only the parents, they will handle the matter. If the police are called, they may let the boy off with a reprimand. Or he may be held temporarily in a detention home or prison until there's a hearing in court. The judge may dismiss the case; or he may put the youth on probation or refer him for treatment to a child-guidance clinic or other social agency; he may place him in a foster home if the family situation is too upsetting, or he may send him to a "training" school.

Just how the boy or girl is handled at any of these stages may have consequences for good or evil. The adolescent is groping for an adult identity. He is being pushed and tugged by conflicting impulses. A boy's rivalry with his father (like a girl's with her mother) urges him to rebel against all authority as arbitrary and unfair. At the same time he yearns — in a part of his mind — to be accepted as a mature member of the community. It may be easy at a certain phase to flick him in the direction of constructiveness or of destructiveness. The manner in which he is treated by parents, police, court people, and others may harden or soften his heart.

When parents discover, through neighbors or the school or the police, that one of their children is accused of an offense (even if it's only stealing trading cards from another child's locker), there are several principles to guide them. They will want to hear his story and show that they trust his honesty if it is convincing. On the other hand, they must persist in getting the whole truth. They should not hold back in asking pertinent questions or allow him to pull the wool over their eyes. For if he is guilty, but senses that they are afraid to find out about it, or are willing to condone it or co-operate in concealing it, he is receiving a silent kind of permission which corrupts his own conscience and makes another offense easier. The parents should insist on prompt apology, and restitution or compensation. This is not to humiliate the child (unnecessary humiliation is not wise) but to have justice done. While the parents are making it crystal-clear that they disapprove of the act and forbid repetition, they should not, in their indignation, behave as if they were totally rejecting him as their child. It is right to assume that there is good in every individual, and it is to the good in him that the parents are speaking. What gets a wrongdoer back on the path of virtue is his need for the continuing love of those closest to him. If he thinks this bond has been lost forever, his antisocial tendencies are free to take over.

The next step is for the parents to try to understand the meaning of the offense. If it obviously signifies only a temporary lapse of good judgment under extenuating circumstances, in a child whose character is sound, there is no need to look further. But if there are further offenses, or if there are other evidences that the child is troubled or resentful or lacking in conscientiousness, outside help should be sought through the school, a family agency, or a child-guidance clinic.

彑 彑 彑

Of those youths who are apprehended it is estimated that the police deal with 75 per cent themselves, without booking them or bringing them to court. It's therefore important that the police have knowledge about the factors which make children behave in different ways, and that they be able to distinguish between those who need only a talking-to and those who are more seriously disturbed, so that they will not pin police and court records on children who show no truly delinquent tendencies. It is even more important that they know how to exert a positive influence on young people. I remember a boy who came from a troubled family and who had been caught in one minor offense. Yet he was a fairly well-intentioned person who responded to trust. The neighborhood policeman had become permanently suspicious of him, on the basis of the single episode. Every time there was mischief or theft in the neighborhood he came to this boy's home, made accusations, and tried to bully a confession out of him. This is not good for any kind of boy. A policeman who goes in for threats and bad names, who takes pride in being feared in the neighborhood, may scare the timid boys. But his effect on the tougher characters is to challenge them to outwit him, to line them up more defiantly against all authorities and the law in general.

The effective policeman is known in the neighborhood as a person who is clear and firm about what is right. At the same time he is liked because he believes there is some good stuff in every young person and appeals to it. The kids on the block are proud of their friendship with him. Through their respect for him they develop respect for the law.

A good policeman is worth several times his salary to the community — in decreasing the financial and emotional costs of today's delinquency and tomorrow's crime. How do we get more good ones? By offering them salaries and respect that will draw mature people into the field and by giving them training in child development.

For those youths who must be held while awaiting court action there should be a detention home, designed to seem not like a prison, providing activities which will keep young people constructively busy, staffed with people who are understanding and capable. There are too few institutions that meet these standards, even in our larger cities. In many places in America, children — to the number of 50,000 a year — are held in ordinary adult prisons, because there is no other place for them. Whether or not a child has serious antisocial tendencies, it is harmful to subject him to the stigma and associations of a jail.

Juvenile courts have been established by law on the sound principle that children up through the age of seventeen should not be considered free agents who are fully responsible for their acts. They are still immature in knowledge, judgment, and self-control. They are at the mercy of their home environment. As growing organisms they are still susceptible of being shaped for better or worse. They should not be publicly branded with police and court records. They presumably need re-education or treatment rather than incarceration. They should not associate with older criminals. So the aim of the juvenile court is not to fix blame and punishment, but to determine what the underlying problem is, to decide whether a change of environment or management, some form of re-education or therapy, is necessary and, if so, to see that it is carried out. The judge should be trained not only in the law but in child psychology. He should have probation officers who are trained social workers to make careful investigations before the hearing and to supervise the carrying-out of decisions. There should be a psychologist and a child psychiatrist on the court staff or available for consultation. In actuality, there are few courts which have all these advantages. The judge may have no special qualifications for understanding and dealing with children. He may not even have legal training. Under the worst of such circumstances, a child can be deprived of his liberty and family and sent to an institution which may be quite inappropriate for him, without gaining any of the supposed benefits of juvenile law, and without the protection of the legal safeguards that apply in ordinary courts. In many juvenile courts the probation officers and other professional people are quite insufficient in numbers and in training.

☙ ☙ ☙

The treatment facilities in the community that are available to the judge are never as ample as he could use. The family and children's social agencies may not be able to provide sufficient counseling services to parents and child. Good foster homes, which are of vital importance when delinquent children's own families are completely disorganized, are difficult to find for even the best of children. It's much harder to find homes that will give understanding care to unruly, unappreciative ones. Child-guidance clinics and private psychiatric care are in particularly short supply.

It's necessary, I think, when mentioning psychiatric treatment for juvenile delinquents (and adult criminals), to make it clear how difficult this is to carry out successfully. I say this because people who have no knowledge of the subject except, perhaps, for a short scene in a movie or television program, may imagine that psychotherapy is a smooth, magic sort of process: in a few sessions the patient recalls significant episodes from early childhood; the wise doctor perceives the connection between these experiences and the patient's symptoms or misbehavior, explains the connection, and the patient is cured.

In reality, even in the most favorable cases, psychotherapy is apt to require appointments at least once a week for a period of one or two years. The past experiences that made a person seriously maladjusted were painful to live through at the time and they are equally painful to recall. A patient soon senses this and unconsciously resists recollecting them. Antagonistic attitudes which the patient developed earlier toward other people are soon being expressed toward his doctor too. In other words, psychotherapy is slow, hard work, for patient and doctor. The patient must have a desire to improve his pattern of life and some readiness to admit that the problem is partly within himself, not all the fault of others. Yet the delinquent is usually in resentful rebellion against parents and the adult world in general. He is not at all inclined to see his own provocation. He rarely asks for psychiatric help, and when it's suggested to him he's apt to spurn it as just another adult trick to shift the blame to him. But the prospect is not as black as I've made out, when the child is basically a fairly decent, conscientious person who has got into trouble through adolescent angriness with parents, or mixed-up unconscious attitudes. In this case he senses the need for help, unconsciously, and he has the capacity to develop trust in the therapist after he has tested him out for a while and found him genuinely understanding. However, on the debit side we know that a psychopath who has never been loved, never had a sense of responsibility, is a poor prospect for treatment. He has no motive to change or even to keep his appointments. Most of the children who become involved in delinquency are neither complete scoundrels nor misunderstood saints. But a majority of them have character disturbances that make psychiatric treatment more difficult than average, so it shouldn't be thought of as a panacea.

Ｍ Ｍ Ｍ

There are two legal proposals that have frequently been suggested when communities become disturbed about delinquency: curfews for young people and laws to make the parents financially liable for their children's depredations. Wide experience has shown that these are ineffective in themselves. A curfew law usually proves to be a nuisance to the families who don't need it but who obey it. To the youths who are on the borderline of law-abidingness it represents a vote of no confidence by the community and a sporting challenge. To those who are definitely antisocial and beyond the control of their parents it is a joke.

Parents who are responsible people are usually quick to pay financial compensation for their children's delinquent acts, quite apart from any law. But those parents who are incapable of exerting control for the good of their children and the family name can't do it to avoid fines either; besides, they often have no money. The worst defect in a parental liability law is that, since most delinquents are rebelling against their parents and unconsciously wanting to hurt them, the law acts as a subtle inducement to the child instead of as a deterrent.

☙ ☙ ☙

The training school in theory is not a prison for punishment though it has to have some security features. Its main purpose is to rehabilitate certain delinquents who, the judge believes, cannot satisfactorily be retrained at home because either the youth is too dangerous to the community, or his family and the neighborhood cannot provide suitable conditions. This is easily said but hard to accomplish. At the sickest end of the scale are a few individuals who are extremely difficult to rehabilitate even with the best institutional environment and psychiatric treatment. They may go on to become habitual adult criminals. Then there is a larger group made up of assorted character disturbances of moderate severity. Various environmental factors have contributed to the delinquency: insufficient affection, inconsistent discipline, disturbed parents, disrupted families, migration to urban slums, discrimination, severe learning disabilities in school. They will usually respond — to some degree — to a wholesome environment and to individual help from a social worker or psychiatrist.

At the healthiest end of the scale in training schools are the youths of fairly sound character who, ideally, should not be there. They have perhaps been the victims of their own impulsiveness or of neighborhood difficulties or of bad luck or of court misunderstanding or court severity. They will often do well enough in any institution. But the experience of having to spend time there will cause a painful impairment of self-esteem that leaves at least slight scars for the rest of their lives.

The running of a good training school is an enormously difficult task. A mother who knows what is called for — in energy, understanding, correction — in the care of her brood of reasonably well-intentioned children, a teacher who knows what it takes to control, instruct, and inspire an average kind of school class, will be able to imagine dimly some the problems of a training school with hundreds of adolescent youths, each one of whom has some sort or degree of antisocial tendency.

Some of them will be rude or sullen or suspicious or aggressive — not just at moments (as in any family) but consistently. Such attitudes are galling, more so to the kind of staff members who are trying conscientiously to be patient than to those who retaliate freely. Dealing constructively with such types calls for an unusual degree of maturity in all staff members, whether house parents, teachers, group workers, case workers, psychiatrists, or administrators. Aside from their technical skills they should have a natural fondness for youths and an understanding of their behavior, a genuine respect for and capacity to evoke the good qualities in every individual, and, at the same time, clarity and firmness in leadership. To put it the other way around, they must not be so insecure that they feel personally affronted or react vindictively to the rudeness and defiance with which they are frequently confronted.

The program of an effective training school has to be many-sided and ingenious. There must be academic courses for those with aptitude, vocational training for others, activity clubs in crafts, sciences, nature study. Many of the boys will be thoroughly discouraged about their learning ability as a result of years of poor achievement and adjustment in school. They will have assumed attitudes of disinterest or scorn. These attitudes can only be counteracted by the designing of courses and activities which inspire enthusiasm and which are at a level that allows the participants to gain a feeling of success.

What I have been describing is an ideal training school. A majority of the ones that actually exist fall short of this ideal to a greater or lesser degree. The shortage of suitable professional workers and house parents who will work in such institutions, for the salaries offered, is desperate. Some schools are hardly different from bad prisons, with a majority of the staff having no training or aptitude, no motivation beyond that of being guards. Under such conditions, the effect of the institution is not rehabilitation. Some of the marginal boys come out more antisocial than when they entered because of the influence of the worst characters among the boys or among the staff members.

⋈ ⋈ ⋈

In summary, where does responsibility lie for the treatment of delinquents? Indignant citizens cry out that it should be the parents'. In that majority of cases in which the parents are sound people they accept the responsibility, often with professional help. On the other hand, we have seen that the parents of most of the serious delinquents are themselves caught up in the same emotional and social disturbances as their children and can't help them without receiving a lot of help themselves. The responsibility then devolves on the staffs of social agencies, guidance clinics, courts, and training schools. But since in a majority of communities the personnel and facilities are insufficient to do the job as it should and could be done, the responsibility comes back to the public. By the public, I mean you and me and the other parents in each locality who care about the future of our own children and the children they associate with. P.T.A.'s and service clubs can arrange talks by professional people who know the local situation, study just what happens in various typical cases, and imagine how they'd feel if these were their own children. There is a lot of ignorance and indifference to be overcome.

To do a decent job, many communities will need to increase their contributions to their social agencies; more local, state, and federal tax funds will have to be assigned to the care of delinquents. But professional people in the field believe that in the long run it would be cheaper to rehabilitate the delinquents who could be rehabilitated but aren't, than to pay the financial and social costs of their later criminal careers.

THE PREVENTION OF
DELINQUENCY

Great changes could be made
if we really put our
knowledge and resources to work.

CAN DELINQUENCY be prevented? That's what parents want to to know most. The prospect may look discouraging. It has been calculated that in American cities today every other boy will come to the attention of the police at least once before he reaches eighteen. (The emphasis is on boys because five times as many boys as girls tangle with the law.) However, a great majority of these offenses can be called minor in the sense that they consist of truancy, mischief, and theft, which do not necessarily spring from seriously antisocial tendencies, though they should still be a matter of concern. I believe that great changes could be made if we really put our knowledge and resources to work.

⟨ SETTING STANDARDS IN THE FAMILY

First let's talk about prevention of minor delinquency in ordinary children, in average and "superior" neighborhoods. Of course, the greatest safeguard consists in the bonds of affection and respect between good fathers and mothers and their children. But even the best children and parents will be influenced for better or worse by the atmosphere around them. I think the easy-come abundance of the postwar years has produced at least a mild letdown in the morale of many people. Parents can best inspire their children with high principles when they themselves feel a part of some common effort, whether it be religious or humanitarian or national. The recent increases in church attendance, enrollment in adult courses, participation in theatrical, musical, and craft activities must represent a spreading desire to find a deeper meaning in life which should eventually be reflected in children. In one sense, a majority of the young people aiming for higher education are taking the lead, for they are studying with a seriousness unknown in previous generations.

Even more important, I think, will be a greater assurance and clarity in the way parents communicate their standards to their children. Unfortunately, many parents have been made hesitant in their leadership by all the teachings and preachings of us child-care professionals. And there has also been a persistent reaction against the righteousness and pomposity that were an aspect of the last century, making many good parents, especially the college-educated ones, almost embarrassed to talk to their children about religious belief, pride in country and obligation to it, devotion to family, the spiritual aspects of marriage, altruism. They have assumed that their children would absorb their ideals anyway. It's certainly true that children do generally conform to their parents' standards, but only approximately. Or, to put it more accurately, since all parents have traces of antisocial impulses hidden behind their good ones, certain of their children may pick these up to a surprising extent unless parents keep clear to themselves and make clear to their children their expectations. The simplest example of this is the unusually polite parents who fail to notice the atrocious rudeness of their child.

🖙 🖙 🖙

I hope you won't take me too seriously if I say that the prevention of mild delinquency in adolescence might start way back in infancy. When a mother, while taking full account of her new baby's individual needs, works him gradually onto a regular feeding schedule, she teaches him that there is a certain order in the universe, and that her needs and her husband's have to be considered. Of course, I don't mean that a "self-demand" schedule lasting for a year or even two will in itself create selfishness. There's still lots of time for learning. But a mother who, for the first two years, completely subordinates her own convenience to her baby's whims is more apt to go on indefinitely in the same relationship.

I'd let a one-year-old experiment gently with stirring his finger in a drop of milk or cereal on his tray, but I wouldn't let him bomb the floor with handfuls or spoonfuls of food — or climb around in his high chair while I tried to feed him, or pull my hair or bite me.

I'd let a two-year-old, who has little sense of property rights, tussle occasionally with a well-matched playmate over a disputed plaything, so that they could teach each other something. But if he were always snatching and bullying, I'd interfere and, if necessary, look for a more equal acquaintance. By three and four, I'd be helping him learn to share; and though I wouldn't expect him to be Little Lord Fauntleroy to adults, I'd be showing him how to be considerate of them. At any age I wouldn't let him abuse his toys or the furnishings or me, though I'd admit to him that every child gets mad at his parent sometimes.

By five or six, I'd expect him to be helpful to the family in small ways, definitely polite to adults, usually co-operative with children. During the elementary school years, when children show a natural interest in rules and ethics and are eager to know their parents' views, I'd define my own standards quite clearly.

After that the going gets tougher because adolescents have a compulsion, at times, to argue not only against their parents' specific rulings but against their philosophy, religion, manners, and way of life. This is hard on certain parents — the ones who are too polite, or too easily convinced they are old-fashioned, or too afraid they might dominate, or too anxious to have their children popular. They back away from declaring their true feelings or giving clear guidance. They don't realize that when adolescents fume this way they are not expressing convictions but quandaries. (When they stop arguing, you'll know they're ready to live their own lives.) It's not that they want to be bossed arbitrarily or talked down to like small children; and their hearts will be hardened by gross unfairness or mistrust. But they do want to know, underneath, what their parents think about kinds of conduct and kinds of people so that they can be guided in coming to the right convictions.

❰ THE CHALLENGE TO THE COMMUNITY

Now we must discuss briefly the prevention of serious delinquency in the community. The highest concentration occurs in urban slums where there is a shifting population with little cohesiveness, leadership, or community pride. New groups are subjected to animosity and scorn. Recreational facilities are often nonexistent. Parental authority is undermined by differing local customs.

A few progressive state and local governments in recent years have set up youth commissions to make surveys of high-delinquency areas, to focus the attention of governmental and private agencies on the local needs, to encourage them to co-ordinate their various services (which sometimes overlap and sometimes leave large gaps), to stimulate the school, church, business, and club leaders in the neighborhood to get together, pool resources, plan youth projects and family recreational activities (taking advantage of little-used meeting rooms and vacant lots, for instance), to encourage the formation of block committees. Any strengthening of the cohesiveness and purposefulness of a neighborhood will be felt in an improved morale in all the families. Experiments have shown that the motivations of most gangs can be redirected into more constructive channels under the guidance of skillful group leaders.

These are all huge tasks, but certain communities have shown that they can be accomplished if there is a will.

¥ ¥ ¥

A majority of the serious and chronic delinquents are boys and girls who have been loved insufficiently, neglected or perhaps abused from early childhood. How can *their* character disturbances be prevented? Their parents usually suffered the same fate in their youth, got little out of school, grew up irresponsible and impulsive, became poor workers, made unstable marriages. So the pattern is passed monotonously from generation to generation. When children are seen to be grossly abused, the court can step in, give custody to a children's agency which will place them in foster homes. This will often prove a satisfactory solution if not too much permanent damage has already been done, and if suitable foster homes can be found.

In the olden days neglected young children were placed in "orphanages" which, incidentally, contained few orphans. But experience showed that few of these institutions were well enough staffed to give children the love, the sense of belonging, the security, that are essential to form stable personalities. Over the years most of the orphanages have closed, and neglected children have gone to foster homes, selected and supervised by a social agency, where they can grow up with substitute parents, in a family atmosphere. But some of these children prove too difficult for any foster parent; and so a few institutions have been upgraded into "residential treatment homes," where expert professional staffs work to rehabilitate them so that they can be cared for in foster homes (or their own homes) after discharge.

But there is always a larger number of young children who are being raised with a degree of deprivation and mishandling which is not sufficiently shocking to justify a court in taking custody but is certainly enough to predispose them to delinquency. I have often sat in conferences with public-health nurses who have encountered such cases in clinics or in their districts. A small child is already showing signs of being mistrustful or mean or uncontrolled. It is suggested that he would profit from attending a nursery school or day nursery. But it most often turns out that there is no high-quality nursery in the neighborhood or that there is no vacancy or that the mother shows little interest. It would be theoretically even more helpful if one or both parents could receive prolonged counseling from a family social agency. But usually they are too disorganized in their feelings and functioning to take the initiative in seeking such help or to keep their appointments. And most family agencies are so busy working with parents who are co-operative that they have little time or inclination to hunt up unpromising clients. One might imagine that irresponsible parents could be made gradually more mature if they could be accepted and participate in group activities in churches and other neighborhood centers. But they are often too shallow and self-centered to be able to make real friendships or to contribute anything to a group.

🎵 🎵 🎵

I have been stressing the negatives because with our present organization of social services we are doing very little to break into these vicious circles. However, those who have worked hard with shallow, irresponsible people know that many of them can be helped to grow up — somewhat — if a professional counselor goes three quarters of the way to make friends, shows great tolerance and understanding, gives a lot, asks little, exerts patient guidance. In a sense you can say that the counselor is providing these childlike people with a parental kind of affection which they lacked in childhood, and this is what fosters a long-delayed growth.

Before we can make a real dent in the steady production and reproduction of chronic delinquents and criminals, we will have to greatly intensify our facilities for reaching these families through expanded social services. This would require increased contributions to community service campaigns and perhaps higher taxes. But I've read that it costs society $30,000 to catch, try, and punish just one felon. You can do a lot of preventing with $30,000.

❨ GOOD SCHOOLS CAN MAKE RESPONSIBLE CHILDREN

Next to the family the most powerful force that molds a child's character is the school. In several distinct ways it can foster his adjustment and law-abidingness or, inadvertently, push him the other way. I myself believe that the most hopeful prospect for reducing delinquency lies in bringing the level of all our schools closer to that of the best.

The proportion of delinquents who have had school problems is very high. The child who can't keep up to the class in his lessons or who is rejected by teachers and classmates for his

behavior is apt to react to the feeling of not belonging by becoming — to some degree — hostile and scornful. His pride
suggests that if he can't be with the rest he can be against them.
Belonging or not belonging to the class at eight years often goes
on to become belonging or not belonging to society at eighteen.
In childhood, school *is* society.

Studies have shown that the teacher's personality and, more
particularly, her basic attitude toward children is a crucial matter. If she (or he) is a critical person who mistrusts certain
children and mistrust her own ability to cope with them, she
gives them a feeling that they are outside the pale, potentially
dangerous. Most of these children, of course, will be stable
enough so that they won't be badly hurt. But there may be several in the class, especially in a troubled neighborhood, who will
move over into the ranks of the teacher-haters, school-haters.
Children who have an antagonistic teacher have more fights
among themselves at recess and after school. The teacher who is
warmhearted makes all the children — well-behaved or difficult,
bright or dull — feel that they belong. The way you get enough
warmhearted teachers is to make teaching such an appealing pro-
fession that a surplus of candidates apply for training, and you
turn down the ones who really don't like children much.

☙ ☙ ☙

There are many factors which can keep a child from succeeding in his lessons. I'll mention only a few. If he is a very anxious
person, or if his early life was seriously deprived, he may have
a limited capacity to pay attention to any subject. There is also
the question of intellectual ability, which varies enormously, of
course. We are apt to think only of the special problems of the
superior child and of the one who is distinctly retarded, forgetting that in the average classroom there is a noticeable difference
in the level of response between the child with an I.Q. of 110
and the one with an I.Q. of 90. Then there are the specific

learning disabilities, particularly in reading but also in arithmetic, which occur frequently, even in children of normal and superior intelligence. Ten to 15 per cent of all boys (and 2 or 3 per cent of girls) have appreciable difficulty learning to read; and since reading is basic to other subjects, too, these children are bound to feel at least some loss of self-confidence, some loss of enthusiasm for school. When combined with other factors this can lead to truancy and other consequences. So a good school or school system should have a psychologist to test children who are not doing well, special classes for those who are retarded generally, remedial programs to come to the rescue of those who have good intelligence but specific disabilities in reading or arithmetic, guidance counselors or school social workers to help children and their parents to find the causes of the emotional factors interfering with school adjustment and, to do something about them, a consulting psychiatrist.

Another vital element in maladjustment to school is poor motivation. This is seen in its simplest form in the child in the early grades who has little interest in learning to read because his parents hardly ever read themselves and have never read a story to him. (We who come from reading families may not realize that the craving to read which we and our children showed in first grade came from wanting to be like parents, and from the joy of being read to.) In the years of the elementary grades, children are relatively docile and most of them do conform, even if they have little enthusiasm. It's quite different in the high-school years when rebelliousness against authority, the desire to get a job and earn money like a man, romantic urges, hunger for excitement, all wax strong. Then interest in schoolwork becomes feeble by comparison unless the family is dedicated to the ideal of advancement through learning. As a matter of fact, even in families of the highest level of education and achievement, an appreciable percentage of the boys run into temporary slumps and blocks in the high-school and university years.

The widespread problem of limited academic motivation is lost sight of by critics of our schools such as certain university

educators, intellectuals, and others who have made great achievements with their brains. They mistrust the efforts of modern
educators to make schoolwork as interesting as possible. They
want our schools to throw out what they call "soft" subjects,
practical courses, "life-adjustment" discussions, and concentrate
on mathematics, languages, and pure (rather than applied)
science. They say that the only valid aim of a school is to train
the mind, that character training belongs in the home. They
object to a child being promoted unless he has clearly passed all
the subject matter of the grade.

What these critics don't realize is that only a small minority
of children have — as they themselves had — the high degree
of intellectual aptitude and academic drive which can make any
abstract subject challenging, no matter how dry it is. If their
recommendations were carried out, the children in the brightest
quarter of the average American school could progress through
to college (though I believe they would show lacks, compared to
the graduates of our better schools, in the areas of initiative, co-
operation, ability to tackle a brand new problem). A majority of
the other three quarters of the children might do fairly well at
first. But by junior high school every class would contain quite
a number of children who had been left back one or two or three
years and were now quite disgusted with school and themselves.
By high school I think that a majority of all the boys would be
either truants or troublemakers or nonparticipating dreamers.

It sounds logical to say that the school's function is to train
the pupil's mind and that his character should be formed at
home. Teachers would be pleased if the problem could be solved
this neatly. But children don't leave their characters at home
when their minds go to school. A fair proportion of them (like
adults) have personality problems of one kind or another that
interfere with their participation. The school has to try to cope
with them, not only to teach them as much as it can, but to keep
the roof on the school. (A college can dispose of students with
academic and behavior problems by dropping them — the public
school has to keep them all.)

Let's look at the methods a first-rate school uses to foster the student's adjustment to learning, to the class, and to life. Teachers are selected who have wholesome attitudes and who have been trained in child development, in the subjects they will teach, and in how to teach them. (The critics who say teachers' colleges waste time on teaching methods only need to visit an elementary classroom to see how necessary the techniques of teaching are.) Classes are small so that the teacher can keep track of each child and individualize his work. The arrangement of desks or tables is preferably flexible so that children who are working at different levels or on special projects can be grouped together, and apart from other groups. In the writing of textbooks and teachers' guides and in the teacher's preparation of each day's work, every effort is made to approach the subject at a level which is right for children of this particular intelligence range, and in terms that will arouse maximum interest and enthusiasm. This is not to make the topic easy but to capture the children's imagination so that they will work and think hard. There are pictures and objects as well as words. Pupils tell of their own experiences and bring materials from home which pertain to the subject. Discussion and reasoning are given more time than reciting by rote.

But these general techniques are not all. No matter how carefully a class is made up of children of about equal ability, there will be differences among them in regard to different subjects. Even in the same subject their ways of responding will vary a lot. To some degree the questions and assignments given to each pupil should be custom tailored. This is where each student's progress can be fostered or neglected, where he can be made to feel like a successful insider or a worthless outsider. What is required of him should be challenging, but it should also be within the limits of his ability. The child who is slow and discouraged in reading but good with his hands is asked to read only what he can do reasonably well. He may also be assigned to a committee which is building a model of the farm they are reading about. His success on the model increases his self-confidence and his sense of being one of the group. In addition it gives him a stronger motive for wanting to be able to read the book about the farm.

In the case, for instance, of a child who is an advanced reader but not popular, the teacher tactfully manages it so that the class selects him to do some extra reading in the library and then to report back to them. In this way, he gets the extra challenge he needs in reading and at the same time advances a step in the estimation of the class. Each of these episodes may seem too small to be important. And it is not that each child is cured of all his difficulties in a few months or even in a few years of ideal schooling. But any mother of a child with a school problem will be able to tell you of the dramatic gains or losses he has made as he has moved from class to class.

Many modern educators are inclined to promote certain children even though they have not progressed well in some of their subjects, *provided* the class ahead has a flexible enough program so that they will be able to continue to participate. This is done because long experience has shown that such children will make more progress under these conditions than if they are kept back, which may bog them down in discouragement. No responsible teacher advances a child into a class where he will be out of contact with the work.

The good school is concerned that each child develop a sense of responsibility toward others, the ability to co-operate with them. He acquires these characteristics not from being lectured to but by having opportunities to practice them. So the teacher must be a democratic leader who encourages discussion, leaves some of the decisions to the group, helps them form committees to carry out projects. Careful experiments have proved that these methods increase the mutual friendliness and trust of the members of any group, and advance their self-discipline — collectively and individually — so that they behave more and more responsibly as the months go by, whether or not an authoritative person is on the scene.

As children get into the high-school years, the differences in their intelligences and particularly in their motivations show up more and more sharply. It has been the magnificent achievement of the best American high schools — over the decades since education to the age of sixteen was made universal — to have worked out a broad range of challenging courses: straight college preparation, general courses with a practical flavor, trade training. This flexibility encourages each student to go as far as he is able, in the direction of his own ambition, under guidance. When well conceived and well taught, such programs have proved their worth in reducing truancy and "drop-outs" to a minimum and in steadily advancing the educational level of our people.

Many localities in the United States are unable to maintain high-quality schools because of a low average income and because the debt limit of the district has been reached. (Since the war, state and local government debt has increased 320 per cent, federal debt 4 per cent.) Yet the nation as a whole is by far the most prosperous in the world and the federal government gets the lion's share of the taxes. That is why most educators and I myself believe that the problem can only be solved, in fairness to all our children, by federal aid to education.

INDEX